OUT OF THE SILENT NORTH

HARRY SINCLAIR DRAGO

SAGEBRUSH
Large Print Westerns

First published in Great Britain by Hutchinson
First published in the United States by Macaulay

First Isis Edition
published 2015
by arrangement with
Golden West Literary Agency

A catalogue record for this book is available
from the British Library.

ISBN 978–1–78541–014–7 (pb)

Published by
F. A. Thorpe (Publishing)
Anstey, Leicestershire

Set by Words & Graphics Ltd.
Anstey, Leicestershire
Printed and bound in Great Britain by
T. J. International Ltd., Padstow, Cornwall

This book is printed on acid-free paper

OUT OF THE SILENT NORTH

T&F

Jim and Diana Stannard were rendered penniless
gentlefolk after the disaster which befell their
father's i estments. Pressured by mounting debts
and main ining the façade of genteel living, Jim
determine to make a fresh start overseas with the
last of th amily's assets — his father's old land
claims in nada. Diana, appalled by the prospect
of a harsl colonial existence, swears she will not
accompan him — but her foiled theft of her
hostess's vels leaves her no option. When they
arrive at tl remote Fort Roubideaux, the pair have
staked eve hing on the possibility of finding gold
on their d. Forging friendships with the local
inhabitant Jim finds himself drawn to the young,
vivacious ench-Canadian Marcette — and when
he is cau in a vicious snowstorm, it is she who
harnesses led team and sets off after him into the
frozen N . . .

TO
ROBERT H. DAVIS
WHO IS NOT ONLY AN ANGLER
AND A GENTLEMAN, BUT
AN APOSTLE OF FRIENDSHIP

Contents

CHAPTER
ONE

Into the Silent North

It was sunrise on the Nishnibottni river!

Early spring was at hand, but it was not a spring of green grasses and warm days. Twice the wild geese, nosing out the Polar winds, see the sun rise and set as they line due north from the mighty St. Lawrence, before they breast the turbid waters of the "river that flows both ways."

So to-day the pale sun searched out a white wilderness and smiled at the glacier-old Nishnibottni as it writhed to free itself of its shackles of ice. Foam white it ran, with a moan like the cry of a woman, and the pounding of the ice floes on the bow of an old flat-bottomed batteau standing its way up the river came like muffled thunder.

Six months ago the sun had gone to grips with the Polar gods and been worsted. And, as he peered through the morning skies he seemed to understand that days there must be, even yet, when a hush and scream would usher down the white hosts of the North with their blinding snow and fingers of ice.

But one there was who stood silent at the door of the *Morning Mist's* wheelhouse who did not know this. He was a stranger, a newcomer to this white land. Spring seemed near to him. He was lost in reflection when, without warning, there came a blast of the whistle. The man jumped. Angus MacNab, master and captain of the old boat, his hand still on the cord, beamed down at him.

"A bonnie whistle that," he smiled. "Befittin', says I, to the best of 'em, and not amiss on this humble messenger of civilization."

Truth to tell, it was a bonnie whistle, with its hoarse throat, and more in keeping with the mighty liners of the kind on which Angus had steamed out of the Clyde some twenty years ago.

"You'll want to be lookin' sharp now, once we round the point. You'll pick the Post up, off there to the right."

The man strained his eyes as old Fort Roubideaux lifted out of the gray dawn, silent and aloof in its wilderness, and his mouth grew grim as he visioned the huddle of houses that banked the old Post. God! What a place! What a place in which to start life anew. The disgust and pity of every mile of this journey — and the miles were many — the very driving need which had sent him here, fermented in his soul at the moment. Jim Stannard had arrived at the end of the visionary rope by which he was to climb to fortune!

He was face to face now with the actual beginning. Work such as he had never known was to hand, and in spite of himself, in spite of all the resolves and the props he had built, he shrank away from this white land before him. Even as he looked, there came sounding

2

across the wastes a cry. Long drawn it was, and rising, too.

Stannard felt little devils racing up his spine. Again the cry came and he felt himself stiffening. He had never heard it before, and even now only half guessed its origin; but from time primeval, with or without previous acquaintance, that cry has come to man with the same meaning. It was as he had guessed — the wolf cry. Not the call of the male, but the long-drawn, hunting cry of a wolf bitch, who had whelped early and had weaned her cubs already.

As he listened for it again the marrow stiffened in Stannard. The fight came back to him — that damnable thrill and urge which had said, go forth and try.

He became aware of the ringing of a bell. Had he not been lost in reverie, he must have heard it long since. Old Nemiskau, the Nascaupee, had been tolling it ever since Mattagami, the Cree runner from the James Bay country, had brought the Factor word of the coming of the packet.

Only twice during the long winter had word come from the outside world. Only death or medicine would send a man on that long traverse to Trois Riviers. It was ten days each way with the dogs, and old Peter's cabin at Lac Ste. Jean, the only shelter, too, and that half-like to be closed if Peter's luck had been good the previous fall. So, long before MacNab's whistle had sounded, Fort Roubideaux had awakened to the importance of the occasion. No man there whose destiny was not in some way linked up with the boat's arrival.

Roubideaux had felt the first tinge of excitement gold can give a primitive outpost. Like its mighty rival, the Honourable, the Hudson's Bay Company, the North West Company controlled the fur industry in this factory, but the hunt for gold was anybody's game.

All winter long big Pierre Baptiste, the chief trader of the Post had driven old man Vallois well-nigh crazy with his pictures of the future when the Copper Kettle country would be overrun with prospectors. It was not idle talk. All of that vast region west of the Nishnibottni, with its hundred creeks, was gold country. Over on the Misstassini the Choate boys had struck the pure quill already.

Tales of "gold finds" drift a long way in the North. Men who had played and lost in the Cobalt and the Temiskaming would be hearing.

"Bagosh you bat ma life dees place gone be beeg town. Tree four 'tousand people, Père Vallois," Pierre would say. "W'at you gone do den? Dose fox and mink she'll all run' 'way!"

Pierre had had plenty to side with him during those long evenings just past. Ritchie, the American, and Conway and Ladue had wintered at the Post, anxious to be the first in next spring.

Pierre Baptiste, mighty, stalwart, dark-skinned, his face scarred by the hundred and one lines with which the North brands her own, and André Vallois, his Factor, thin, gray-haired and wiry, were a picture of contrasts.

André had come into the North, as all boys do who are sired on the lower Saguenay, and found it to his liking.

From a white house in Chambord he had taken his bride into the North. They had fared well together. Years went singing by. When the big timber along the lower Nishnibottni was gone they had moved again.

North, always North, the call had been. Here at Roubideaux André had prospered. "Pearl of the North," men had called his little Mariette. But the time came when it was demanded of her, as it is of all pearls of price, that she make the great sacrifice. There, in the dimly lighted room, holding André's hand to the last, she had slipped away from him. But she had not made the sacrifice in vain. A little black-eyed baby girl had come to take her place.

The North is crude and its manners rough. The wonder, then, that André Vallois found so many ways in which to be tender, so many kindnesses to make life possible for the little black-haired youngster, Marcette.

Girlhood, almost womanhood, had come to her by now. She was proud like her mother, with that same beauty of eye and body. And eighteen is an age of expectation. So if the coming of the river boat meant much to old André or Pierre, or the many others at the Post, it most surely meant more to little Marcette.

There would be clothes, bonbons — many trifles. But these were minor things if Marcette had known. She was hungry for others of her own kind and age. Romance? It was a word she was not familiar with, but Père Vallois sensed a change in her as they waited for Captain MacNab to come swinging up the steps of the Fort.

Her father knew the outside world was always a place of mystery and adventure in the eyes of youth. But never in the past had the coming of the spring boat, with news of it, excited her like this.

Stannard, from his position near the wheelhouse, was an interested spectator. Marcette dropped her eyes when she became aware of the man, and saw that he was looking at her. Her father felt the fingers tighten, *"Mon père,"* she cooed, *"mon père,* I am so happy."

He was good to look upon, this Englishman. Marcette dared another look. A queer little ache stabbed her as she saw a well-groomed, smart-looking girl come to his side. She saw the man's face relax at her approach and noted, too, the arm that stole about the girl's waist.

What she said to him, Marcette could not hear, for the voice was low, well modulated, obviously a cultured one. But she heard the man say, "Well, Diana, we will go down, eh?"

Captain MacNab met them at the stairway. A miniature explosion startled them. "There goes old André's cannon," he laughed. "We'll be goin' ashore the noo. If your luggage is ready I'll be takin' your teekets here, and once the rest of thim have gone ashore, we'll go and meet old Andy and yonder bonnie lass."

Diana gave him one of her rare smiles. Smiles had not been one of her noticeable assets the past few weeks.

"Right you are, Captain," she said. "Luggage all shipshape. I'm ready for the worst. Jim —"

6

She stopped short as she caught the whiteness of her brother's face.

From pocket to pocket Stannard's hands were traveling until they were grotesque in their movements. Diana caught at them.

"Jim?" she questioned excitedly, some of her brother's panic communicating itself to her.

"My wallet," he gasped, "it's — it's gone."

Diana was beside herself with anger.

"My word, Jim! How could you be so careless? Look again! What will we do if it's really gone?"

Captain MacNab got into action.

"Mr. Stannard, sir, let's be methodical. Now, one at a time, we'll try the pockets."

And, suiting the action to his words, he began going through Jim's clothes. It availed nothing. The wallet was gone.

"No one will be goin' ashore till we find it, my lad." Old Angus was beginning to boil. "Close onto fifteen year have I been runnin' this packet, and she's been an honest place for honest folk and no one can say me nae. I won't be changin' me feathers this late. Do you stand to lose any great amount by this bad turn?"

"Just about everything," Jim answered. "Cash — some six hundred pounds: deeds to the property which brought us here; all the proof of our assessment work done in the past."

He stopped and gritted his teeth even though he hung his head. "What devilish luck," he muttered, "and you, Captain — the tickets they are gone too!"

"Nae, you won't be reminding me of that again! Well I ken ye had them."

Stepping to the rail, he bellowed to Davie, his mate: "Watch sharp there, lad! Nae one ashore e'en if you have to use yer fists."

"What's all this deuced delay for?" asked a passenger, who came dashing up the companionway. He was a man of thirty-five or so, and a queer cross between the well-bred Englishman often seen in the North and the French Canadian of the fur country. In dress, he had adopted the picturesque features of native attire. It gave personality to Ashleigh Nafferton.

Five years is quite a space of time in the North, and Nafferton had turned many sharp curves. He honestly believed he had acquired the bigness of the country he had adopted. He was mistaken. The Northland soon takes its own to its heart. Nafferton was only play-acting. He could not fool men like old André or MacNab.

Diana turned a tortured face to him. Nafferton had scraped an acquaintance with her brother during the long wait at Trois Riviers. He and the Stannards had mutual friends back home. That is an open sesame in the wild. Nafferton was not blind to Diana's charms. Pretending to be familiar with the creek country at the headwaters of the Nishnibottni, he had arranged to go in with Stannard.

"Why, Mr. Nafferton," she said petulantly, for Diana was thoroughly angry with her brother for what she deemed his carelessness, "Jim has been simple enough to let someone rob him of his wallet."

Nafferton was almost earnest in his solicitude.

"You don't mean it, old fellow?" he asked.

"Right enough," Stannard answered. "Cleaned out. Broke! Stone-broke in the Far North."

CHAPTER
TWO

Like a Play

Jim Stannard, in spite of the light tone, was stunned. Being broke in the Far North carried with it a threat of disaster beyond the present and into lives other than his own. It was with an effort he looked at his sister. This venture had been forced through against her wishes.

"Of course something like this was bound to happen," she half sneered. "It's the luck of the Stannards. These men should not be allowed to leave the boat until they are searched."

Quite a crowd had gathered, and MacNab waved them back.

"I wouldn't put it past any of them," Diana continued. "They look as if they'd stop at nothing. Are you afraid to assert your authority, Captain?"

"That's it!" Nafferton echoed. "Search them."

"I hae me doubts about some of them being willin' to let you go through their pockets. As for their looks, set no store by that," MacNab suggested. "But it's the only way. The skunk that nipped the purse we may be sure ain't man enough to come forward with it.

Stand to, there!" he roared at the crowd about the rail.

The boat had nosed into the landing and the deck hands stood ready to throw out the gangplank. MacNab walked across the deck.

"It's a shame to ask ye, men, but I guess there's nae ither way out. An honest mon can nae object to being searched."

There was a half-hearted acceptance of this. Murmurs of objection followed. One man, a thick-set fellow of middle age spoke up: "*Sacré!* I have not got de man's monee. You know that, MacNab."

The man was Honest Dave La Pointe, the whitest saloonkeeper north of Trois Riviers. He was a hard nut to crack, if he wanted to be stubborn. He had a reputation to sustain.

"I'd stake a lot on you, Dave. But we can't make fish of one and flesh of another."

"By Gar, *I* not be gone through this way!"

Nafferton was quick to aid in the searching of his fellow passengers. He was in his element, his nimble fingers dipping in and out of the willing pockets of those lined up against the rail.

He neared La Pointe.

"Why you be so dam' anxious to pull everything out?" he asked Nafferton.

"Don't be stubborn, Frenchie," Nafferton replied brusquely. "Stand over there and wait your turn."

"Who's going to search you?" La Pointe questioned. "Who knows — maybe you tak' de purse. You were closer to it dan any wan else."

Nafferton was bending down over a prospector's open dunnage bag. He paused, to answer, but Diana laughed La Pointe's suggestion to scorn.

"Mr. Nafferton is of our own party. It's absurd to think of searching him."

The nimble thoughts of Nafferton kept up with his equally nimble fingers before he arose.

"I'm willing," he smiled, opening his coat with a flourish. "Here, Jim, go through me."

"I won't hear of it," Diana protested. "I'll never speak to you if you permit it, Jim Stannard." Her languid beauty was displaced by a tigerish look that revealed her in the old light to her brother. Jim brushed La Pointe's insinuation aside as unworthy.

"Mr. Nafferton does not need to be searched. His word is good enough for me."

"But my word, he is not good enough, eh? Who make the fish of one and the flesh of the other now, Captain MacNab?"

"Hold your horses, Dave. He's the doctor. This is his friend, his partner."

Diana tried to end the episode by saying with a tone of finality:

"It is not for you to question what we do."

The blood jumped in La Pointe at that. That tone and manner did not belong in the North. Here one man was as good as the next. Did she think he was a servant?

Nafferton had gone down the line by this time, and as Diana spoke, he had inserted his hands into La

Pointe's pockets. The next instant he was sprawling upon the deck.

With quick decision Stannard advanced on the Frenchman.

"But you must be searched, my man," he said quietly. The use of the expression "my man" was unfortunate. For answer La Pointe made a pass at Jim that would have sent him to join Nafferton, but for a sudden jump, accompanied by a swinging blow that caught La Pointe on the jaw.

The force of the blow was a surprise to his antagonist, judging by the look on his face. In a second La Pointe had squared off again and was at Stannard. MacNab held Diana back as the two men circled each other, their breath coming in long-drawn gasps. Diana had never witnessed a fist fight. Yet for all its crudeness, it thrilled something primitive in her.

Jim closed in again and caught the heavier man on the jaw. La Pointe rushed head down, then. Stannard stepped lightly aside and landed a terrific blow upon the man's ear as his rush carried him by. His own momentum and the force of Jim's blow carried La Pointe off his feet, and he rolled to the deck.

In answer to Jim's question if he would submit to the search now, La Pointe yelled to his compatriots and whipped out a knife, Diana screamed. She pushed Nafferton forward: but as he hung back a great hand fell upon La Pointe's arm.

"I tak' dat *couteau*, La Pointe!"

The man had climbed up the side of the *Morning Mist* from the landing below. After he had possessed

13

himself of the knife, he turned to those who were about to spring to the assistance of their vanquished friend.

"Eet was a fair fight. You saw heem. Dave ees willin' to fight when he think he can win, but *mon jee*, he wants to be a butcher eef he lose."

The giant Frenchman towered head and shoulders above them.

"I'm glad you were on hand, Pierre. It might hae turned out nasty," MacNab said. Turning to Jim he introduced the peacemaker.

"Pierre Ducet, Stannard! He is a man ye can well tie to, that's if he'll let you."

Jim reached out his hand. Diana sniffed superciliously.

"Do hurry, Jim," she interrupted. "This is getting on my nerves."

Nafferton joined the group, his work done. Even the obstreperous La Pointe had been thoroughly searched for the missing purse which had not been found.

Nafferton tried to buck up Jim with a pat on the back. "Don't worry, old man. I can let you have a hundred now, and even a bit more if you need it. In a pinch, you can sell your outfit for nearly what it cost."

Jim shook his head. "I've made it a rule of my life, Nafferton, never to take another loan. When I do, I sink. It will mark low water for me."

"Jim, you are ridiculous," Diana asserted. "By your own carelessness we are here, strapped, and if Mr. Nafferton is kind enough to advance you a sum like this you cannot refuse it."

"No go, Di! We'll get by some way. I've got the outfit, and if Nafferton sticks, I'll do as I intended. We can

14

make arrangements with the Factor to look out for you. You would be more comfortable here at that."

"You'll do, me lad," MacNab asserted. "You've got the pluck to win out."

Diana caught Jim by the wrist. "You don't mean to say that you are going to try and go through with this thing. How can you make it? We must live — eat! It can't be done. Mr. Nafferton's suggestion was logical. Sell this mess of tools and dogs and return to Quebec or Montreal for a year or two. You can make another start later. You have got to think of me, Jim!"

Stannard squared away at that.

"I am thinking of you." The force of his words held her motionless. Even Nafferton was caught by it. "We go on!"

The gang-plank went slithering across the landing. Old Angus nodded to them. "No bit use hanging back. When the milk is spilt 'tis ever best to be about getting more milk."

"Funny though, isn't it?" Jim laughed. "Like a play, 'Broke in the Far North!'"

"Ah! You've got the pluck, laddie. And there is one thing they won't be takin' awa' from ye."

"Yes?" There was a question in Jim's eyes.

"Friends! You'll hae friends in the North and it's nae sich a bad spot whin ye hae friends."

CHAPTER
THREE

To Hold an Ace

The call of the North has been heard by many who did not stop to weigh its trials. They *had* to come. To others it has been a hide-away, a refuge from the law, or debt, or prying eyes. To many it has been a land of promise where fortunes were to be made in a hurry. To a few it has been a scourge, a place of dread and privation.

To the latter class Jim Stannard belonged.

It is a long cry from Piccadilly and the gaieties of Ascot and Epsom to the wilds of Northern Canada. Culture, refinement, ease, and once even affluence, had been hand-maidens to him since boyhood. Canada was a torture to be taken like medicine, endured and placated that it might be made to yield him his share of its riches.

England — London — held every interest in the world for Stannard. Never a day dawned but a dozen little voices called to him to come and play. Races, theatres — the country with its house parties, horses and hounds — they were his life.

England, because it was England, was his England.

The need must have been great to have sent him this far afield.

Money — that was it. He needed money — great quantities of it. Canada was his only chance.

A night three months gone had decided him to go back.

He and his sister were house guests at a weekend party the Mannings were giving at their country place in Devonshire.

The play had been high that night. Luck, as usual, steadily against him.

He needed an ace. He remembered that.

Hypnotically, he stared at the card he had drawn — a deuce!

The two little red spots wavered, ran together, blended, became one. The multiple heart, symbol of love and luck, continued its delusion.

It was an ace, then!

His well-sculptured hand shot out for the money piled high on the table.

"What are you doing, Jim? That's not an ace."

The voice brought him back. The hand poised midway. He looked at his card again. The perspiration broke on his forehead. It was a deuce after all!

"Of course not," he replied, nonchalantly, "I — I was merely helping Blackledge to gather in his spoils. But you do not want my help, do you?"

There was an insult in the question.

"You are so infernally used to this er — sort of thing."

A sardonic smile hovered for an instant on the lips of the honorable candidate from Manchester. He nodded as he piled the bills and coins and Stannard's note for five hundred pounds into a neat stack.

He shuffled and re-shuffled the cards. Stannard's I. O. U. held his eye. The amount was really a trifling sum, but it meant power. Just another little stepping-stone in his social progress.

He paused as if pondering a question.

"Stannard, do you want a chance at that I. O. U.? I'll risk it against those worthless claims of yours in Canada."

The insult was studied.

Stannard made to rise. "Your generosity is appalling," he said defiantly.

"Why not? It's a chance."

"For two reasons, — because they *are* worthless, and because my father didn't think so."

"Oh, anything you have then, if you feel that way about it," Blackledge persisted.

"I might put up my cuff links," Jim answered easily, as if dismissing the possibility of a wager.

Blackledge dealt then and purposely left him out. A slight flush mounting his cheeks, Stannard arose. From the half-contemptuous shrug of the shoulders, Blackledge knew that he had gone a step too far in his attempt at humbling him.

One by one the other players gave excuses and went to join the women.

"A lot of damned aristocrats," was Black Oliver's comment. Yet in his heart he knew it marked the difference he would have given all of his money to erase.

18

Like most men of humble origin, who have won the smiles of fortune, Oliver Blackledge sought to blot out the memory of his beginnings.

There were certain financial deals, too, that were best forgotten — even the one which boosted him into the peerage.

Stannard's set held him a bounder, a low person. One to whom it was not well to be indebted, for he would have his pound. Or what was much worse, its equivalent.

Diana stopped her brother as he left the card room. She knew the signs. "Well?" she queried.

"It's five hundred. To Blackledge, too, worse luck."

"Why don't you be more discriminating," she smiled at him, lest someone sense the seriousness of the discussion. "Blackledge is the one person in the world to whom I should hesitate to owe five hundred pounds or five hundred pence. Why didn't you — hold an ace under cover?"

"Would you?"

Where was she drifting to voice such a thing?

"I wouldn't lose. Not to Blackledge. These new peers are notorious scandal-mongers. It is a case of noblesse disoblige."

"Listen, Di, would you hold out an ace?"

"For heaven's sake, don't pull that long face. They'll think you have decided to take holy orders. You'd look well in the cloth."

Diana Stannard's rippling laugh caused many heads to turn.

Jim was beside himself. "You don't know what you are saying. You frighten me. How far would you go — for all this?"

It was an all embracing gesture that took in the suave, idly chatting groups, the steady-glowing candelabra, the furnishings of exquisite taste.

Diana took his arm. "To the foot of the garden where we might talk it over without taking every one into our confidence."

"Don't!" he muttered. "Your sarcasm is ghastly. I want to be alone. Here comes Malcolm for you, anyway."

His eyes followed the graceful girl as she crossed the floor. He wondered who among all the men fluttering around her would be willing to marry her, if he knew she was a penniless hanger-on.

That's what she was — a hanger-on.

So was he.

He had no more right there than a navvy. Only his intellect, his training, his culture, his ancestry of gentlefolk allowed him to cross the threshold.

He felt his world tumbling about his ears. He wanted to be alone. He wanted to think.

The air was sweet with the perfume of roses as Stannard sought solitude in the moonlit garden.

They were near the end. He had known it for some time. Why were fathers so frightfully careless in their investments? Did they give no thought to their children, when they imperiled their entire fortune?

Jim had once worn the purple on a charge account he never had to face. Six months had passed since the disaster, which had left him penniless and the mainstay of his sister.

They had emerged from the many meetings with their solicitors, unchastened. For six months they had gotten on. Their credit with the tradespeople, their adroitly dovetailed house parties and the slim bank balance had sufficed.

Stannard knew that they could not have done otherwise. Here he was, his only assets those of a gentleman. What could he have done then, or now? He knew nothing of work or trade. His sister even less.

Why did people continually invite them about? Diana was popular. And himself? Didn't they suspect?

And how he loved London and the life of ease and refinement which had always been his! He could almost reconcile himself to his sister's state of mind.

"God!" he muttered. "The issue has to be met. I can't keep my self-respect and go on. This living at the social free-lunch counter is only dodging the end."

It seemed hopeless.

"If I could only get away! Get away for a new start. That's it," he murmured. "Canada — those old claims of father's — sell what few things we have and make a try for it. It wouldn't have to be for long. We could come back. God! for a time when I could buy — spend money without the haunting fear that it was taking food out of her mouth."

He trembled as he thought of the struggle it would be to make Diana see it his way.

Someone was calling him. It was Ken Manning, his host.

Even in the dim light of the garden Stannard could not conceal from his keen eyes his air of depression. Something was amiss.

"What's wrong, old fellow?"

Ken was a gem. No pretense with him.

"Oh, the same old thing, Ken." Stannard's voice was bitter. "Just to the end of the rope, this time. Blackledge got me for five hundred."

"Well, we can fix that up, I guess. Can't have you owing him money. What have you done about it?"

"Gave him my note." He laughed sarcastically.

"And —" Manning questioned.

"Ken, you know, the note is next to worthless, that I can't meet it."

His friend's tone was vexed as he answered, "I heard a breath of this. Why didn't you come to me, Jim?"

"Who has been talking?"

"That's not the question. You didn't take me into your confidence when you were short. An old pal wouldn't go in for that, if he was really a pal. Not after all these years. You know what I mean."

"Of course I do, Ken." There was a little smudge of emotion on Jim's lips that passed with the rapidity of such things among Anglo-Saxons.

"Prove it," rejoined Manning, crushing a note for a thousand pounds into his fingers and turning away.

Stannard felt the crinkly new bill in his hand. It brought him up short.

"I can't take it, old man. There is not a chance that I could repay you."

"Don't be foolish, Jim! What are you going to do?"

"I'll tell you, Ken, what I am going to do." He was almost vehement in his sincerity. "I'm going to pull up stakes. I'm going to sell off the things we have left! Pay up the debts and that note of Blackledge's and clear out for Canada. The pater always thought well of his property out there, and I'll make a go for it."

"Do you know anything about mining? I mean, outside of what scanty knowledge you got at school?"

"No! But I'll learn. Diana will go too."

"I'm not sure that's best; but pray, from where will all the money come for this?"

The question was put in all kindliness.

"It will take a smart sum. You'll need an outfit and all that sort of thing, Jim" — Ken's voice quavered a little — "Take the thousand. You'll need it and Cecilie would never forgive me if I let you go without it."

That was a new angle — Cecilie.

Both of them were silent for a long time. It was Jim who finally said: "Ken, I'll take it. But there are two conditions — that Cecilie never knows. And that you never make me another offer like this. Is it a bargain?"

CHAPTER
FOUR

The Honor of
the Family

The banging door behind her brother told Diana she was alone. She threw herself on the bed, and bit into the pillows like a child.

The North! Canada! Poverty and mean struggling! Becoming a colonial. That's what Jim's dictum meant. She would refuse to go. At the last minute something would turn up. Jim might change his mind. At that thought, she winced. She knew her brother. Once he set out on a course nothing could alter his determination. Anyhow, she would refuse to go. That was settled. She could not face life away from the people she had always known; the friends she meant so much to. This made her pause. How much did she mean to any of them? All they cared for was form, pleasure. That meant the right sort of people and gaming, dancing, dining. Well, these made the sum total of existence. She was going to have them. How? She didn't ask herself that question. She only knew she wasn't going to Canada.

She repeated this over and over until she became hysterical. Tears had long since ceased to relieve her.

She pounded the glass top of her dressing table so violently that the knuckles of her beautiful hands bled.

"I'll die before I do this thing," she sobbed. "I'll run away — I'll marry . . . I will! . . . even Blackledge!"

She gritted her teeth as she thought of the oily Oliver, with his millions. She knew he would come running at a sign from her. Hours dragged by as she goaded herself to further misery and then sought equally to find a way out. Dawn found life had still refused to become an orderly thing, yet here was the maid packing her things.

Without interest, she heard her say that most of the other guests were ready for leaving. She looked at herself in the large French mirror. She was a sight. Begrudgingly she gave herself over to be turned out as best she could. A half-hour later one would hardly have suspected the agony she had gone through.

She saw Jim pacing back and forth downstairs. His face was drawn and tired. She heard someone moving in the next room. Evidently Rose Cheever was up, and leaving, too. She could confide in Lady Cheever. Her ladyship had even plead Sir Oliver's cause at one time. Doubtless coincident with a heavy loss at bridge by herself.

The maid left as Diana dabbed a last bit of powder on her neck, telling her that the heavy luggage would be to the station in plenty of time. She called her back to give her a pound note. The queer light in the servant's eyes seemed to say that she knew how lonely the note's existence had been.

25

Diana found the door of the Cheever apartment ajar. She tapped lightly and entered. She was surprised to find she was alone. Pausing on the threshold, she was about to call out when her eyes became fascinated by a chamois bag that lay on the top tray of a half-packed trunk in the center of the room.

Slowly, like a bird charmed by a snake, she advanced toward it. Her feet fell noiselessly on the carpet. She glanced furtively toward the bedroom, and thought she heard someone moving inside. Was it the maid, or Rose, herself?

For an instant she stood irresolute beside the open trunk. The pupils of her eyes contracted into points of fire. Here was a way out! A way even better than Black Oliver with his bovine manners. Her thoughts raced, trying to weigh the consequences. She thought she heard Jim calling. Instantly there rushed back into her mind the memory of what he proposed doing with her. It decided her in a flash. With a swift gesture she bent down and swept the jewel bag into the bosom of her dress.

Jim wondered why Diana seemed so nervous when he met her hurrying along the hall.

"We're leaving in an hour," he announced. "Had breakfast yet?"

"Just came from it," she lied and hastened away. "I'll be ready," she called over her shoulder.

In ten minutes the house was in a turmoil. Lady Cheever's jewels had been stolen! Ken and Cecilie were badly upset. The guests were asked not to leave until the detectives arrived.

"It wasn't burglary," Lady Cheever wailed. "It was just plain sneak-thieving. I left my bag on the dresser —"

"On top of the trunk," the maid corrected.

"Well, whatever! I had not been gone from the room more than five minutes."

"It was ten, m'lady," the maid corrected again. "Just about ten minutes. I was busy with m'lady's clothes in the boudoir. I thought I heard footsteps in the other room. But wasn't sure. Anyhow, I believe at the time I didn't pay any attention as I thought maybe m'lady was back."

She was a sour-faced, elderly woman who had been with the Cheevers for years. There was no question of her veracity.

Jim asked her if any one had called on Lady Cheever since the night before. It was a natural question, but focused attention on him.

"No one visited m'lady," the maid asserted. "I was in the apartment from eight o'clock."

Against his will Stannard knew his eyes were searching Diana's face. It told him nothing.

"Looks like the work of a sneak-thief," he muttered and turned away.

Downstairs he found the butler.

"My sister was not well last night, Robbins, and I hope she doesn't eat a thing for twenty-four hours. You didn't insist on her taking breakfast?"

The butler shook his head.

"Miss Stannard has not even looked in on the breakfast room this mornin'," he assured Jim. "I was thinkin' of arskin' about her, as it's quite a step to the station and a long ride to London . . . that is if you haven't eaten a bite."

"No need to worry, Robbins. I'll see to her."

With murder in his heart he sought his sister. She was in her room, putting on her hat.

Jim locked the door on entering. He stood in the middle of the floor and surveyed the headstrong, petulant girl his father had recommended to his care. How he had failed, that she should come to this.

"Where are they?" he asked quietly.

Diana's well-rounded under jaw moved nervously, but no sound came from her lips.

"Did you hear?" Jim repeated. "Where are they?"

"What?"

"You know what!"

Brother and sister looked at one another. She was a Stannard for all her faults.

"I don't know what you are talking about," she said with determination.

Jim advanced and bent over her.

"I'll cry it out at the top of my voice so all can hear unless you give them to me at once. I believe Rose Cheever would have you arrested."

"Your silly theatricals amuse me," Diana said unctuously. "Cry out so that all can hear and see if you do ought but soil yourself. What proof have you that I am responsible for the loss of her precious jewels?"

"Proof?" He shot the word at her. "Robbins tells me you never set your foot in the breakfast room this morning. You and Rose's maid were the only ones upstairs at the time."

Diana's face blanched.

"Now shall I cry out?" Jim asked.

"No, no! My God, no!" she beseeched him, covering her face with her hands as if he might strike her, so wild were his eyes. Diana broke down and cried.

"No hysterics," Jim warned her. "Get the bag."

He almost whispered the word. The terrified girl pointed to a drawer. Jim found the Cheever heirlooms hidden among some laces. He slipped the bag into his pocket.

"Even if these are returned, there might be some desire on the part of the police to know the truth of the theft. Fortunately for us, we leave for Canada in ten days. You have made it your own choice."

It was with some effort that he induced his host to go with him to the Cheever apartment and make a thorough search.

"You know how these hysterical women are," he announced. "They don't know where they put things half the time. Let's look everywhere before the police arrive."

With difficulty the Mannings persuaded Lady Cheever to consent to the arrangement.

"We have searched everywhere," she scolded.

"All the pockets?" Jim questioned, his hand bulking large in his own coat while he spoke.

"Don't talk nonsense, Jim Stannard! Who puts a bag of jewels in a pocket?"

"Some do for convenience," Jim asserted. "Others from compulsion — and others from —"

"I do believe this has affected your brain," Lady Cheever interrupted, testily. "But have your own way. Search everywhere. It will do no good. Lucy and I have gone over every inch of the rooms."

With Manning's help the Cheever possessions were thoroughly searched. The jewels were finally discovered tucked away in a corner of the trunk, and ten days later Jim and his sister sailed for Canada.

The voyage to Quebec, the stay in Trois Riviers, the long trip up the river, were only milestones in a pilgrimage of dread.

And now at last they were here at the edge of the world, penniless, forlorn. No wonder Jim shuddered. It was as he said: "like a play."

CHAPTER
FIVE

Pierre Baptiste

"*Sacré!*" the Factor laughed. "What you care? What I care? What anybody care? Up here we freeze outside; but we thaw inside, M'sieu'. Don't forget that. Shake hands!"

Jim held out his hand half-heartedly.

"*Non, non!* So."

Stannard essayed an imitation of Père Vallois' hearty manner.

"That's better. Now again. Good! Smile when you do it. See?"

He grinned until his strong healthy teeth showed.

"Back of your smile, keep your thoughts. Don't forget that. A man measure good at first, or he not measure. The little things he do tell you all about him. *Vraiment!* Because he think not at all when he do them. Watch when he eat, or light his pipe — or speak to pretty women! — it tell you all you want to know."

A week had passed since the arrival of the spring boat. Jim had rented a comfortable cabin within the Post for his sister and himself. Diana still found life drab enough during the long days, but even she was not proof against the glowing wood fires in the quiet evenings.

At this time there were some two hundred people in and around the Fort. Until after the arrival of the fur trains from the James Bay posts, the population of Roubideaux would not vary much. There must have been ten or twelve white women of one kind and another there that spring; but of them all little Marcette was the one Diana chose as her confidante.

The English girl was a revelation to the Factor's daughter. Never before had she seen such fine clothes and those delicate things every woman appraises for their true worth on sight.

Within her was being born the desire to make herself a great lady, too. Marcette had quite forgotten that childish pang of jealousy she had felt the day the Stannards arrived at the Fort.

People had talked for a time about the robbery, but even in the North, to-day's happenings belong to to-day. Old MacNab had not overstepped himself when he declared Jim would make friends.

André, Pierre Baptiste, MacNab and Jim were seated before a roaring fire in the Post trade-room. The wild wind outside and the flaming fire within gave one such an air of security that talk flowed easily.

It was big Pierre who answered Père Vallois.

"Bagosh, dat's true, M'sieu'. All hover de Nort' I hear men say 'Bo' jou', Pierre Baptiste!' and me, I mak' no meestak'. I see dat look in some eye lak de *chasse gallerie*, or de *loup garou*, and me mak' no friend dere."

He turned to Jim. *"Mon Dieu!* You look sharp dat time you loose dat money, you catch dat look somewhere. Me — I don' half look and I guess I catch heem hall right."

All three chairs came down from their tilted angles at that. Angus spoke.

"Am I hearin' you richt, mon? You say you ken who did it?" Pierre smiled.

"His name?" Père Vallois demanded.

Pierre Baptiste knocked the ashes from his dead pipe. *"Non, non, mon père,"* he answered. "To know a t'ing ees to know heem. To say it, ees to prove. Me, I cannot prove dis; but, some wan was in dose Nascaupee lodges by de river yesterday. An' de t'ing he want to know ees, how you fin' de way to Windigo creek. Now dat's a funny t'ing. Anybody in Roubideaux wan' know how get dere come ask me, first t'ing sure pop."

"Well, what do you think it means?" Jim asked, catching the hint of suspicion Pierre was throwing onto the wind.

"Who knows?" Pierre Baptiste shrugged his shoulders. "No one mak' any talk 'bout goin' up de Windigo but you M'sieu', and —" Pierre hesitated — "and your — er — er — friend M'sieu' Nafferton. You know damn well *you* don't go by dose Nascaupee lodges. Your friend goin' guide you dere, he don't have ask no man how hees goin' get dere, hey? He tell you he know all 'bout dose creek. So I say, eef you don' ask no question, eef M'sieu' Nafferton spik de *truth* an' don' have ask any: an' somebody wan' find out 'bout dat country an' am 'fraid ask me — *mon jee!* I know dere's sumt'ing wrong."

MacNab puffed his pipe in silence. Père Vallois knew from his manner that big Pierre had not finished. He saw him regard Stannard, who sat with puzzled brow staring into the fire.

The few days at Roubideaux had developed a lot of talk about his property on the headwaters of the Nishnibottni.

A hundred small creeks, like peas in the proverbial pod, dot that land. Men who had run trap lines there, winter, after winter, and who knew the country as only a woodsman can get to know a region, would tell you that it was a place of horror for a tenderfoot.

Pierre had trapped and panned and even driven a drill over the best of it. He was chief trader to Vallois now and apt to know what was going on in the Post.

"I'm afraid you are unduly suspicious," Jim said, as he arose to leave. "It never occurred to me to ask about our route. Mr. Nafferton assures me he knows the country and I believe him."

He stopped short and shot an unexpected question at Pierre. "You don't like Mr. Nafferton, do you?"

"So?" The big Frenchman countered.

"Do you know any reason why I should not trust him?"

It went against the grain with Stannard to discuss a man he considered his friend. Still he felt the innuendo in Pierre's talk.

"You say I don' lak' dis M'sieu' Nafferton." He was picking his words rather carefully. "Maybe eet ees,

M'sieu' Nafferton does not lak' me, *n'est-ce pas?* He does not come here. *Mais;* I don' say, don' trust heem. In dees country ever' man must fin' dat out heemself. But I do say, dat de man who was in de Nascaupee camp was no Frenchman. I was pretty far away, but I know he was no Frenchman."

"What makes you so sure?"

"Because de *bott' sauvage* don't make no mark in de snow lak' dat. Hees an Eenglish heel, dat mark."

From his pocket Pierre produced a stringed pouch of generous size.

"Here is little ting wan of dose Injun boy pick up." He handed it to Stannard.

It was an old hat check from the Carlton in London. Jim knew it for his own because on the back of the card he had scribbled the telephone number of a racing acquaintance — Mayfair 3216.

Any doubt that lingered in his mind was gone. The man who had robbed him was still at the Post. Pierre's information placed the theft at the door of one of his own race. Or — and the thought was one which did not seem to hold water — perhaps the big fellow was trying to throw suspicion on another man to protect himself or a friend.

Stannard had been overjoyed to sense the big Frenchman's faith in the ultimate prosperity of the upper Nishnibottni as a gold field. Ritchie, the American, was another optimist. Ike and Eddie Choate had proved the worth of the Misstassini. Jim knew the gold craze well enough to understand that as soon as a claim becomes of value men are ready to barter their lives and honor for it.

During the days which followed, Nafferton proved himself to be a capable outfitter. To Jim's way of thinking he spent too much time in Dave La Pointe's saloon, their quarrel a matter of the past. It was a matter of a man's choice, at that. But Nafferton's avoidance of the Factor and his trader was too noticeable to escape his attention.

He spoke to him about it one day. Nafferton had a plausible answer to hand.

"It's intentional on my part," he said. "Get friendly with old Vallois and we'll be pestered to death with advice and don'ts. He's a talky old man, and his chief trader not much better in that respect. If he feels he has a string on us, there will not be a company runner, trader, trapper, or Post Indian who will not feel called upon to look in on us when they go through. You may find your claims are worthless. The ones next door may be bonanzas. We want a chance to nose about unhampered. If we do hit it off, the news will come through quick enough without old André's assistance."

Stannard had to admit the good logic of his statement. As often happens, Jim had seen only one side of a possible condition. Yet Nafferton had voiced a half-truth only. If the old Factor should evidence an interest in them, were they, so to speak, under his wing, it is also true that he would stand by them in the matter of help when they needed it. The possibility of needing help is never so remote in a wild country like this, that one can afford to ignore it.

Nafferton had really made a technical error in holding aloof from old André. Of course, what he feared was, that some of his escapades had come to the ears of the old man; most likely recalled by his chief trader.

Nafferton had lied to Stannard from the start. He knew nothing of the country to which he proposed to take him. His mining experience was nil. Flying to whatever chance offered to make a dollar, come as it might, it was not to be expected that he could acquire knowledge of any particular thing to a degree to make it worth while.

As a matter of fact, the worst either Pierre or André could bring against him was a general knowledge of his worthlessness. It was not Stannard, but his sister, who had first attracted Nafferton and led him to risk the adventure. An *entente* between Diana and himself was what he wanted most of all. He had not made a mistake in believing he could capture her.

The girl's appraising eyes took cognizance of the goodly height, the breadth of shoulders, the nice modulation of voice, which mark the man of culture, be his morals what they may. He was the sole representative of her type of civilization, outside of her brother, with whom she could come in contact.

There was something of the primitive in her that answered to the devil-may-careness of Nafferton.

Marcette watched the growing intimacy with alarm. She, as well as Pierre Baptiste, had caught that wild light in the man's eye.

"That M'sieu' Nafferton is bad man," she said to herself. "Ver' bad man."

As the day for her brother's departure drew near, Diana became morose. She could have stood to lose Jim without too much emotion; but to have both Jim and Nafferton taken away, filled her with dismay.

"What will I do when brother and Mr. Nafferton leave?" she said to Marcette one evening. "There must be someone here who knows something besides the price of skins — or how many quills a goose would have, if it had twice as many as it has."

Marcette was puzzled.

"But we have here only the goose to eat, Ma'm'selle. The wild goose," she reiterated.

Diana smiled at her literal interpretation of the symbol of the goose quills.

"Who knows anything here? — I mean among the men," she persisted.

"Pierre Baptiste!"

Marcette knew what she was talking about now.

The English girl had to laugh at Marcette's enthusiasm.

"He knows everything," she went on. "By one look at the sun he tell the time. When he pick up a handful of snow, like that — he blow it so, and tell you, we have more snow to-morrow. If he say snow — it snow. And when the beautiful spring comes he speaks with every flower. He knows them all by name. He take any trail, any time, like he not know one from the other, but he never get lost. He is always right."

It was not knowledge of this sort, that Diana sought. Big Pierre was dross to her.

"I hate people who are always so confoundedly right," she said.

"You surely like Pierre Baptiste," Marcette insisted. "Everybody like Pierre."

"It wasn't personal," Diana answered. "In England we used to hang people who were always right — right about stupid things."

"What he knows is not stupid." Marcette would have dared battle on this subject. "He has saved the lives of many people because of what he knows, way out there." She made a gesture in the direction of the interminable miles of wilderness outside the Post. "To do that is not stupid."

Marcette was too primitive to conceal her resentment over what, to her, was a slighting of big Pierre.

"Pierre Baptiste say it is not well to go now. We have big storm in two, three day. The fur train from Pointe Aux Barques should have been here yesterday. Pierre say they wait, because they know snow is coming and it is best not to risk it."

"That's your native for you," Diana answered aggravatingly. "Always foreboding unpleasant things."

Marcette drew her parka close about her as she prepared to leave.

"Maybe so," she said half angrily. "But if they go and the storm comes and catches them, you will cry your eyes out, and these men here will not move an inch to find them. They will say it be no use to try. But Pierre, the stupid, he'll go." Under her breath she added — "If I ask him."

"Good night," she finished aloud. Before Diana could answer she was gone. A moment later she heard Marcette's heavy little shoes crunching the snow.

CHAPTER
SIX

Before the Storm

Marcette drew the parka's hood low over her face as she hurried along. For, although the snow was fine, it was icy sharp with a bite only known in northern latitudes. To protect herself she lowered her head. She knew every foot of the way and did not need her eyes to guide her. Thus it was that she did not see the stalwart figure coming toward her.

It was Stannard on his way to his cabin.

Jim was lost in thought and gave as little heed to his progress as did Marcette. Rounding the corner of the storehouse they ran full tilt into each other. Marcette felt herself lifted and set firmly upon the ground. She looked up to see Jim's smiling face peering down at her. For a second his arms had been about her, and even in her surprise, she remembered their strength with a warm glow of happiness.

Stannard's eyes sparkled as he beheld her. She was such a little thing and so much a part of the night she walked in. He felt as out of place beside her, in this wild land, as he knew she would have felt in his old haunts.

"I'm so sorry," he laughed, and smiled apologetically, "my thoughts were miles away."

There was a good, clean, whole-heartedness in his laugh. Marcette wondered if the princes she had read about talked as he did. Words were melodies coming from his lips. How unlike her father and Pierre he was. And yet, he was not like Nafferton. When he looked at her she felt delightful waves of emotion passing over her such as she had never known.

She laughed, too, and a real laugh to match his own.

"The snow bite so, to-night," she smiled, "I shut my eyes and not see where I go."

"Are we in for a real snow?" Jim asked.

Snow now would mean more delay for him. "We want to get away day after to-morrow."

"No. Too cold to be big snow. But this snow soon make it warmer, then maybe we get the big storm."

Marcette wondered if she dare ask the question on her tongue. Naively she put it. "M'sieu' Jim, you won't go if the storm comes?"

Stannard thought he felt the fingers on his arm tighten.

"Why, yes," he said simply. "We've got to go. I haven't the money to risk waiting."

"Men get lost and die in bad storms this time of the year." She broke off. "Pierre Baptiste say we are going to have very bad storm."

"Maybe so," he answered doubtfully. "Nothing is certain in the North. I've learned that already. But come — let me take you home."

He gave Marcette his arm. Never before had any man offered her such a courtesy. It took her back a little. It was pleasant, though, she thought, to walk like this. She wondered if he guessed how unfamiliar she was with the ways of ladies and gentlemen.

A minute or two sufficed to bring them to the door of the trade-room. He swung the heavy door for her and with an engaging smile left her to face big Pierre, who sat alone finishing his last pipeful.

He regarded her with mingled emotions. Marcette was changed. His little girl was gone. In her place had come a woman who thrilled him with her beauty and feminine graces.

He watched her now as she undid the high goloshes and shook the snow from her parka. Her eyes shimmered like crystal; sure enough sign to Pierre that she was past the girl stage. He had seen that light in the eye of a doe just before the mating season.

Silently Marcette came to his chair and knelt at his knee as she had done for years past.

Minutes rolled by before either spoke as they continued to gaze at the dying fire. As was his way, Pierre placed his heavy hand on her shoulder. At that Marcette turned and looked up into his eyes.

It told the man beside her as plainly as the printed page can tell the scholar, that she was in love, and his own heart sank like lead. For he read in her look that it was not of him she thought.

Willingly he would have given his life for her, and the sacrifice would have counted as nothing with him. With as little hesitation, he would have killed for her sake. He knew the way of these chechakos in the North. It was not jealousy that fired the thought. He had travelled the land he loved and he had seen. Most of them were there only for a day.

"Wat he say to you, Marcette?" he asked. He stroked her hair with his giant hand as he waited for her answer.

"He say very little, Pierre. He just look at me and smile. But his eyes were so sad. And when he look at me that way," she cuddled her arms to her breast to illustrate her words, "it make me feel so funny. Just like he was a little baby that I got to take care of."

She felt the big man repress a sigh and did not guess what it cost him.

"What makes M'sieu' Jim so sad?" she asked.

Pierre thought before he answered her. "A woman, perhaps. Who knows? You t'ink young man lak' heem leave England wit'out leave behin' wan girl?"

She had not thought of that. The sharp pain that accompanied this question of Pierre's almost ended the conversation for the night. She arose and stood staring into the embers.

Pierre arose too.

"Dis Nafferton, hees frien' — he's a rascal, a *loup garou*. You look to yourself when he ees by, Marcette."

"*Oui*, I look, Pierre. Do not fear," she replied. "He is a fool — a younger son fool. M'sieu' Jim be very sorry some day he ever listen to him."

"*Bon soir, ma petite*," Pierre nodded. "I watch heem."

There was little sleep for Marcette that night. Before daylight she heard the faint cry of men coming over the trail which came west across the barrens from Fort

Revillac. In a minute the cry was clear: *"Vive le Nort'westaire'! Vive le Revillac!"*

It was the fur train from the shores of the Vermillion. The cry, the old battle call of the N. W. Company.

At its head came Jean Cour, the blowhard, the drunkard. He was the butt of many a joke, even in the North, with his red sash and brass jewelry. But his fists were hard and he was not a coward.

Nafferton gazed upon him with awe. He was the *courier-de-bois* of old to his unpracticed eye, the very man to lead him to the Windigo. Over their cups in La Pointe's bar the pact was sealed.

Pierre Baptiste clicked his teeth when he heard of it. He knew Jean Cour, and that he had never set foot on the upper Nishnibottni. Pierre regretted the fact that Père Vallois was sending him away to Lac Ste. Jean. Some days would elapse before he and Mattagami, the Cree, would return. He would have liked to have told Stannard the truth.

The following morning Nafferton and Jean Cour had things ready to get off. Père Vallois watched them in silence. Diana and Marcette were there, too. The English girl in her undemonstrative way had said her good-byes the evening before. She knew several months, or more, would elapse before their return.

With a wild hurrah, Jean Cour swung his whip, and the huskies leaped away. Their trail for a day and a half was a well-trodden one on which the dogs would eat up the long miles.

Marcette's cheeks still burned with the blush Stannard's good-bye smile had sent to them.

45

From Diana's window they watched until the team was almost out of sight. True to Marcette's prophecy, the weather had warmed considerably.

Diana noticed her quietness. "Why so blue?" she asked.

"That Jean Cour drink too much to be good guide," she confided. "He hide many bottles of the white whiskey in his sled. I am afraid. My father tried to stop him. He just laugh when I say we have very bad storm day after to-morrow. If the storm comes, and that Jean Cour is very drunk, it be very bad."

Diana did not combat her statement this time. In silence, the two girls watched the little speck that moved across the snow. As they watched Diana became aware of the regular drip, drip, of water.

"What's that?" she asked, startled.

Marcette drew in her breath. "The snow on the roof is melting. It is getting warmer. Pierre was right. It will snow."

CHAPTER
SEVEN

The Devil's Bedroom

Two nights in a sleeping-bag had rubbed the smile from Stannard's lips. He shivered as he drank the scalding hot tea and munched the dry bannock.

A hush, — as if death walked on the air, — hung about them. It seemed that the world waited for something untoward to happen.

Jean Cour was too happy in his surreptitious intercourse with the white whiskey to heed the signs he could read as a child reads its story book. Nafferton and Jim rolled their bags and strapped them down as the Frenchman buckled the dogs into place.

He sang that wild chanson of the *courier-de-bois* about the beautiful belle of Trois Riviers for whom he vowed he'd swim the rapids of the Cheval Blanc:

"*Ma Belle, Ma Belle, Ma Belle Julie!*"

He roared as he fumbled at his work.

Nafferton and Jean had fallen out the previous day. Drunk, and thick-witted as he was, he saw through the Englishman. He saw also that the dogs were going lame and it riled his blood.

Red stains marked the crust where they trod. Jean swore. At increasingly short intervals he had to use the lash.

"The dam' fools," he reiterated, monotonously, "the dam' fools."

The time soon came when even the whip failed to move them. He caught up the leader's fore paw. The pad was worn off clean.

He turned to Nafferton with an oath. "You dam' fool! For why you not run dose dog little while each day and harden up dere feets? Huh? You chechako! Now we wait t'ree, four hour while I mak' some boot for dem."

Hours passed as Jean Cour cut and fashioned the rude boots from a fur robe. He packed their tortured paws in lard before drawing them on. The warm lard and the leather pads were only a makeshift at best. The life was gone out of that team for days to come.

Their speed of yesterday had been terrific compared with the snail's pace they were forced to now.

Stannard had dog-trotted beside the team for hours on end. His strength surprised him. Nafferton was in a nasty mood. He felt that he had lost prestige in Jim's eyes by the turn things had taken.

A frozen fish apiece for the dogs, and hot tea and pemmican for the men, marked the noon resting. It was a silent, ill-humored group.

As they sat there lamenting their position, a wild humming as of many telephone wires began. The hush was gone. The humming grew and grew until it became a scream. Jean Cour jumped to his feet. He realized too late his negligence.

48

The storm predicted by Big Pierre was upon them.

Out of the North the hounds of the air raced madly, white frost hanging from their angry jowls.

The spot where it caught them was well within the gates of Jacquard's Pass. For two days they had been heading for it. It was the objective of all trails into the North out of Roubideaux.

Since the days when old man Jacquard had named it after himself, trailers were wont to call it "The Devil's Bedroom."

The name was at least illuminative. For five miles it cut through sheer walls of basalt worn smooth by the elements. Coming in from the south there was not a nook or cranny to hide in. At its northern entrance, however, there was a little park of cedars and lodge-pole pines cunningly hid away in a tiny elbow of the pass proper.

It was a place of refuge in a storm like this.

The dogs howled as Jean laid the whip on them. Sore feet or not, they had to travel now. Again and again he lashed them, until Jim grabbed the whip.

The Frenchman turned with an angry snarl. "Dere's timber four mile ahead," he bellowed. You had to yell to make yourself understood. "We got to git dere or die!"

Jim strained his eyes ahead but could see nothing. Even the high walls of the pass were veiled by the white clouds that rushed by him. It was a straight chute for the wind, which with an ever-rising cry came screaming down from the polar zones lifting a smother of snow and banking it into an impassable barrier.

Stannard appealed to Nafferton. Needless to say he was for turning back. From the depths of his parka, Jim heard him shout: "The wind's in our teeth piling up a mountain ahead of us. The fool has lost his way."

Jean Cour, in a frenzy, mushed trail and howled at the dogs until the perspiration dripped from his forehead. His parched throat cried out for relief. He dropped back to his bottle.

Nafferton was begging Stannard to turn around. Anything was better than facing that sheet of blinding snow. "My God!" he moaned; "let's up-end the sled and crawl into our bags. The dogs can look for themselves. This Frenchman's a fool!"

A grim smile, which curled his blackened, bleeding lips, stole over Jim's face as he regarded the pitiful figure of Nafferton. He saw him then for the weakling he was.

Jean Cour heard that word "fool." He knew they were talking about him. He rushed at Nafferton.

"Wat you say 'bout me, hey?" he cried. "Wat you tell heem 'bout me?"

The Frenchman raised his hand to strike. Jim caught his arm and tried to calm him, but he could not keep him still.

"Bah, you're a lily pad — a daffodil," he shrieked. "Wat you do up here wit' dose baby eye? You belong back wit' de girls dat sing. You piano player, you!"

Jim turned Jean around and motioned for him to start the dogs.

"It's not the time for rowing. We're going on." Nafferton could not hear his words, but he caught the significance of his gesture. Stannard had heard tales of men who had resorted to their sleeping-bags, as Nafferton suggested, only to be dug out of the drifts months later.

On and on they toiled as the snow piled up in front of them. Every foot of it was an uphill climb. Jim mushed trail beside the guide. It was a heart-breaking experience. Being new to it, the little economies of energy the practiced hand may employ were outside his knowledge.

Every yard gained was as a mile in the making. Jim saw Jean flounder and fall. The guide tried to rise and then sank back contentedly to the soft snow. Jim knew they must be two miles from the timber. He tried to get the man to his feet. The overstimulation of the whiskey had brought its reaction. He looked around for Nafferton. The Englishman was gone.

Jim bent over the inert Jean Cour. He shook him. "Wake up!" he shouted in his ear. There was no answering sign. He beat him then until his fists ached. With the Frenchman out, he knew they were done for.

It occurred to him that the hair of the dog which bit Jean might do the trick. He reached for his flask and poured its contents down the guide's throat. In a minute or two he sat up and opened his eyes owlishly and very gravely winked at him. Under other circumstances Stannard could have laughed.

With returning consciousness, Jean reached out for his remaining bottle. The dogs felt the hand on the traces and turned, upsetting the sled.

With a grunt of dismay, Jean Cour fell back, groping with both hands, for the bottle which Stannard sent scurrying into the snow.

The dogs ceased their scrambling and settled down, their backs to wind, waiting for their lord and master to get his senses and cut the traces.

Darkness was beginning to hedge them in. Stannard stumbled to where the dogs lay. His foot caught and he fell. He lay there lacking the will to rise. How warm and soft the snow was! It seemed like a gigantic feather bed. Where was Nafferton? He wondered if he, too, had found a nice warm bed like this.

As he pondered, there came on the wind a cry that he had heard once before. It crashed with menace against his ears. The dogs stiffened. He struggled to his feet.

He cut the heavy leather traces with his knife. Immediately the dogs circled, back to back. They knew that cry for what it was. Hunger was in every note of it.

He tried to find Nafferton.

The dogs moaned as he wandered away. Once he thought he heard the cry of a child. He listened and heard it again. Laboriously he turned his feet in its direction. Before him appeared a man crawling on his hands and knees. By his look he was mad. It was Nafferton.

Helping him as he could, Jim circled back to where the whining dogs sat stiff-legged. He laughed. He was going back to his warm bed. Bed! That was it. He wanted to sleep. Sleep? He couldn't keep his eyes open.

What was the use anyway? Cecilie would marry someone else and Diana would get on some way without him. Yes, Cecilie would forget. The thought was insistent.

He found the sled and crawled beside it and snuggled into the robe which had become undone. Millions and millions of feathers were plucked from celestial birds and tossed down to make him a pillow. The overturned sled kept the wind off. That terrible wind!

He fancied he heard a voice. It was old André's daughter. He smiled at the hallucination. She had warned him. He remembered that. How helpless he was compared with her. She was the best thing in this damned land, anyway. No, not the best thing. The snow — the nice, warm snow was the best thing. He burrowed his head in it and slept.

CHAPTER EIGHT

The Way of the Wind

Back at Roubideaux, Marcette had waited and watched. Until evening the dripping eaves sounded their warning. Morning came and again they started their knell of drop on drop.

Gray and heavy grew the skies; but not a flake fell. By noon the hush of their coming began to rest on her ears.

She mapped Stannard's progress in her mind. Every difficulty and delay she allowed for. If they would only get through the Devil's Bedroom before it broke they would have a chance. As the hours dragged by and the air held clear, she prayed that they might make it. Another six hours and they must run through.

She wondered why Stannard's safety meant so much to her. Nafferton she despised. Jean Cour only excited her pity. Why did men always have to pay for the foolhardiness and ignorance of others, she asked herself.

She caught sight of her heaving breast as she gazed into her little French mirror. The tomboy part of her was gone. The blood left her face as she thought of Jim out there in the hands of Jean Cour.

54

She remembered his sad eyes and their far-away look; the kindly mouth with its hovering smile; the rugged chin that at times seemed cruel.

What kind of a woman could have put those lines under his eyes and that look in the eyes themselves? The big world outside must be a strange place to do that.

Noon-time came and she bade old Nemiskau get her dogs ready. Since yesterday an idea had been revolving in her mind. She had known all along that she would do this.

Silently she stole about the Post gathering food for the dogs and herself. Nemiskau knew he was tempting fate in not telling her father. If he had seen the food hidden in the sled he would not have held back even though Marcette had bullied him since babyhood.

Père Vallois saw her as she sped through the inner yard of the Post. He yelled and commanded her to stop, but Marcette only waved her hand at him.

Once she had topped the rise back of the Post she lined straight for Lac Ste. Jean. A wild fury possessed her. The snow began to descend. She laughed hysterically. No girl in all England could help him now. She alone could save M'sieu' Jim!

From the first her plan had been to follow Pierre's trail to Lac Ste. Jean; to intercept him as he dashed back to the Post, and to implore him to rush to Stannard's aid.

She knew Pierre would read the signs better than she. For a certainty he would be heading back to Roubideaux rather than risk being snowed in for a week or two at Henri's cabin, thereby forcing upon himself that long, arduous mush back home.

That he might refuse to go to Stannard's rescue, even for *her* sake, did not make her hesitate.

Almost to the hour she had foretold the coming of the storm. If Pierre had left that morning, as she believed he had, they ought to meet at Caribou Rocks before nightfall.

She refused to think of the fate that awaited her if they missed each other. By the way it was coming down the snow would be deep enough to call for real, man-sized mushing by the time she reached the Rocks. For all her native ability and strength, she knew she could not match herself against that task and win out.

Like a liaison officer of the first water, she built an hypothesis and staked her life on it.

On her fifteenth birthday, now some three years past, Pierre Baptiste had given her a husky pup sired by his own great dog, Empereur, up to that time the best wolf-crossed dog in the North. Napoleon, the pup, had taken the laurels away from his father. Pierre broke him to lead, and dropped her old leader, Honorine, back to be sled dog. Honorine was almost pure wolf. To find fit running mates for them old André had dug deep into his purse. So, to win her battle, Marcette had on her side her light weight, and a dog team second to none.

Her father had watched her out of sight knowing full well no team he could muster could overtake her were she minded not to stop. He vented his anger on Nemiskau. The old Nascaupee quailed before the Factor's wrath.

Marcette was no load at all for the mighty team. 'Poleon flattened his ears, and Chichi and the other dogs, back to big Honorine, settled down to a mile-devouring pace. They bent their heads as the fury of the storm smote them, but did not slacken their speed.

The trail had been well packed, and the driving wind behind the snow swept it clean long after it had begun to bank elsewhere. Marcette knew the trail would be blotted out soon. A crevice here, a hollow there, would serve for a resting place and bit by bit the drifts would grow until the white horde had won the day.

Once 'Poleon stumbled. Before she could pull him up he had regained his feet, and Honorine, snapping at the heels of the dog ahead of her, straightened the team out, and off they flew.

The leader had learned his lesson, and he fought his way through the growing drifts with care. Marcette shuddered as she realized that the barriers were getting more frequent and harder to scale.

Soon they ran into drifts that left the dogs floundering in the white fluff. Marcette mushed them out. It used up all the energy her little body held.

Came a long pointing to the windward, then, swept clear as ice. Darkness hung above her. She remembered this long stretch to the North. Another half hour would bring them to Caribou Rocks.

Another half hour would tell the story. Marcette repeated her thought aloud. They had not passed each other; either Honorine or 'Poleon would have winded old Empereur.

An hour from now it would be black night. She knew she dared not leave the meagre shelter of the Rocks once she had reached them. Safe there, she would be a prisoner. Days would elapse before the snow would crust enough to carry even her light body. Starvation faced her in that event.

"Oh, Mother in Heaven!" she prayed. "Pierre — Pierre —" she muttered as the dogs raced along.

The cold bit into her flesh. She buried her face in the robes to protect it. After an interval she felt the dogs slacken and heard Honorine yelp as the sled trod her hindquarters. The team was tangled up by the sudden stop.

" 'Poleon, Chichi, François!" she shouted; but the dogs refused to move. Marcette got to her feet. She realized then that they were out of the wind. The hungry dogs hung back in their shelter.

Cold fear struck the girl. She stumbled ahead. They had come to Caribou Rocks! Where was Pierre Baptiste? She swept the plain below them with her eyes, but nothing moved. Wherever she looked the white land mocked her.

She mumbled a prayer. Mechanically she made a lean-to of the sled and cleaned the snow out of a cavern in the rocks. She threw the dogs their supper and from the sled drew forth firewood enough to boil the tea. She rolled herself into her heavy robe and waited for the water to heat.

She thought of her father, of Jim, of Pierre. She could not understand why he had not come. Maybe he was sick — or an accident. 'Poleon growled, as he tore at the frozen fish. Honorine held her nose high into the air. Sniffing, she walked to where the wind struck her. She drew in a breath that sounded like the sucking of a bellows. Marcette watched her, spellbound, as the head went up again and the mouth closed. A second elapsed, and then followed the long, booming cry of the wolf-dog.

Marcette strained her ears for the answering call. Faint and far away it came.

She ran to the dog and hugged him as the tears fell from her eyes. Someone was coming!

'Poleon sprang erect and gave voice to the wind. Louder and louder he bayed. And then again the answer came. Nearer and near it sounded.

Father and son were calling each other.

CHAPTER
NINE

The Spirit of
the North

A white giant strode into the faint light of her small
fire. The spirit of the polar gods sat on him as he stared
from his mantle of ice and snow at the figure before
him. Palsied fear smote him when he recognized her.
He tried to speak, but his voice failed.

Marcette sprang into his arms. The hot tears ran
down her cheeks as she snuggled close to him. She was
a baby again. Fear was gone. No harm could come with
Pierre beside her.

Père Vallois' chief trader was dumb with amazement,
although his heart warmed within him. His little girl
was back! Even so, she had come to him in the past
with her troubles.

"Je ne comprend pas!" he cried. "Marcette, w'at all
dis mean? Why you be here lak' dis?"

Another figure stalked into the light of the fire. It was
Mattagami, the Cree. He grunted in surprise at the
sight of Marcette. Without more ado he went searching
for firewood he had cached there.

The tea boiled as Marcette explained her mission to the man beside her. She discarded the cumbersome English for her native French. The eyes of Pierre Baptiste narrowed as she went on. She was a woman, after all, and not a girl. What could a man do to compare with them in the way of sacrifice? Frail and tender as she was, she had dared what few men would attempt, and the end was not yet.

But how, he asked, was he to do this thing? Jacquard's Pass was miles away. The long trail by Rolling Stone sure to be waist deep in snow by the time they reached it. If Stannard was lost, finding him to-morrow morning would be too late. Better not to go at all than to risk their lives on an errand he knew beforehand was destined to result in failure.

He envied Stannard. He prayed, for Marcette's sake, that the Englishman would turn out different from the run of his kind in the North. After to-night, let him take care. He would answer to him, Pierre Baptiste Ducet for any slight he put upon her.

Pierre wondered if Stannard realized what he had awakened in Marcette. The Englishman had the calibre of a man about him for all of his tenderfoot ways. He had an air of reserve that appealed to the big Frenchman. But child of impulse that he was, Pierre Baptiste could not help but feel that Marcette was building an air castle which would collapse about her own head.

He drank the hot tea in big gulps and smoked his pipe as the Cree fed the fire. What Marcette asked meant the risking of three lives. Only luck could lead them to Jacquard's Pass in time to be of use, and then it was no certainty that they would find Stannard there.

Pierre knew he would do as she asked. It was not of himself he thought. What was he to do with her? As bad to send her back with Mattagami as to take her with him. Leaving her here was out of the question. Pierre needed the Cree if he was to have a fighting chance of getting to the Pass.

Marcette came near to him.

"Dis English Jim, he mean so much to you, eh, Marcette?" he asked. "You ris' your life lak' eet was pinch of salt?"

Marcette did not answer other than to bury her head on his breast. Pierre babied her as was his way. *"Ma petite, ma petite,"* he crooned, and was silent then for a spell.

"Mon Dieu!" he ejaculated at last. "Don't ever let heem know you do dis."

For ten minutes he had been devising a way to reach the Pass in time. It was done subconsciously. Aloud, he spoke to Mattagami, in Cree. From his own team he took Empereur and cut out one of Marcette's dogs, to find room for 'Poleon's father.

He transferred what food they had to Marcette's sled. It went against the grain to leave his own dogs behind, but they would only be in the way were he to take them. He took their collars off, and knew if they were not forced to battle with the wolves they would eventually show up at Roubideaux. His own sled he turned bottom side up.

Marcette had named a task for giants. Could the best dogs in the North and Pierre and Mattagami, as famous as they were, win through?

Cold and dreary the little shelter was, but it took courage to face that branding wind and storm-swept tableland above them. Pierre strapped Marcette in the sled. They were ready to start. He bent low so she could hear.

"Marcette," he said, "eef we get dere, an' you live, don' evaire forget dis night. I do sumt'ing for you now, I nevaire tink I do for any wan. No use to tak' trail by Rolling Stone. We be too late even eef we git by.

"Six hour from now we got to be where we're goin'. Me an' de Cree are good for t'ree hour apiece ahead of dose dogs. No man in de Nort' could do more in dis storm. So we go straight crost de tip of de Lac. Dere's beeg cracks in dat ice. Five, ten feet wide. Maybe now, some snow-ice fill 'em up. We' tak de chance.

"Eef we have good luck on de ice, we'll go right over de top of de hills till we come to Jacquard's old shanty. Den de trail into de Pass where dose cedars are. I guess we find 'em dere hall right. Eef not we look in de Pass.

" 'Poleon, allez!" he cried. The dogs strained at their breast-straps and were off.

Back to the shores of Lac Ste. Jean they went. Less than an hour had elapsed since Pierre and the Cree had mushed that trail, but already it was half obscured. Still the advantage was a great one.

Every ounce of strength and minute of time saved now, the Frenchman placed against the hour when they should win across the lake. Delays he knew would face them on the ice. There lay the great danger.

From Lac Ste. Jean to Jacquard's shanty it would be brute strength alone that would win out.

From time to time Mattagami and Pierre rode the sled for intervals of a minute, where the going would permit of it. It saved their wind and brought relief to their eyes.

An hour from the time they started, Pierre caught sight of the ash thicket which marked the shores of the lake. Here they left the trail to Henri's cabin.

Try as they would, they could not keep the sled from burying itself in the heavy snow banked under the shores of the lake. The dogs floundered in it helplessly. They pulled Marcette out of the drift, sputtering and waving her arms.

Twenty minutes later they were on the ice. The wind tore at them now with redoubled fury. It seemed at times that they could not stand against it.

The ice, swept clean, spread out before them, a sheet of smudgy white. Only the testing of weight itself would tell them, too late, that they had ventured in the wrong direction.

Eagle-wise, in his knowledge of ice and the wind-rows under such conditions, Pierre led them on. Speed was their best safeguard now. Minutes went by. Appeared before them then the shadowy bulk of high hills.

But even as Pierre prayed that they might get by without accident, Mattagami went slushing through to his waist. The Frenchman threw himself flat on the ice

64

and reached out his hand for him. Like a beaver, the Cree caught it, and crawled over the prostrate Pierre to safety. Hurriedly the Indian dried himself as best he could. Five minutes later his clothes were frozen stiff to the waist.

Back and forth they explored the extent of the open water. They detoured for better than a mile to pass it. Pierre knew the danger grew as they neared the shore. Time after time they stopped.

The wind was less wild. They were crawling into the lee of the high hills before them.

Pierre strapped on his snowshoes to spread his weight as he tested the ice ahead. Mattagami waited with the sled and Marcette. They heard Pierre's halloo as he reached the bank. In a few minutes he was back on the solid ice opposite the trap between them. He bade the Cree cross as he had done.

He called the dogs then. At a bound they jumped. Five seconds brought them across in safety, but in back of the dogs Pierre could hear the water sucking down the soft slush ice which had broken under the weight of Marcette and the sled.

The Indian's legs bothered him. Pierre dosed the Cree with his flask.

Came work now such as he had never known. Fury fought fury as they toiled for the summit of the hills. Angry blasts caught them and tried to drag them down into the white abyss from which they were emerging.

Up and up they went, until Pierre leaned against the scarred spruce which stands at the crest. Perspiration dripped from him. Marcette's heart struck her as she gazed on Pierre. What had she asked of this man? Who else in all her world would have thus seared his body for her?

She brushed her way into his arms. Pierre felt her warm lips on his own. It was the elixir he needed to make the fight to the finish.

"Gran' cœur — Gran' cœur!" he heard her say. "Great heart — Great heart!"

It was his due.

Once more they went forward. Moments came when it seemed they must give up. The mind lashed the body. Wearily the tired flesh responded.

Out of the encircling darkness a house loomed. It was Jacquard's cabin. Mattagami was in such condition that Pierre decided to leave him there. The old cabin was a haven of refuge. Wood was to hand; the Cree would pull through.

Like a plummet the trail dropped into the Pass. Pierre rode the sled as it pitched down the sheltered path. He was almost asleep as the dogs pulled up among the cedars and small, lodge-pole pines he had headed for, hours back at Caribou Rocks.

He found an old lean-to he had built there the previous Spring. Marcette used her snowshoe, shovel-wise, to dig it out of its nest.

Pierre left her and searched the little park.

He was back shortly. They were alone. He refused to look at the girl's eyes. His own were tired and sunken; all emotion had long since fled.

Down into the Pass he wandered. He must have traveled half a mile when he fell. Something lay beside him in the snow. He looked and saw the white face of Jean Cour staring at him. Wild fear was in the glaring, open eyes. Life had passed.

Pierre found the sled then. The dogs were gone. Doubtless to the rugged caverns above where they could fight for their lives.

The big man struggled to overturn the heavy sled. He felt beneath it. His hand encountered something warm.

He heaved with his shoulder and the sled fell away. Jim and Nafferton lay before him. Buried in the robe, Nafferton on top of him, Jim had slept. Slowly, at aggravating intervals, his lungs expanded. Life still flowed.

Nafferton lay motionless, the white pallor of death hovering about him.

In Pierre's absence Marcette had worked like a beaver uncovering firewood. She fed the flames as they leaped high. Pierre caught sight of her fire. Like a drunken man he stumbled and lurched toward her. Marcette saw the limp body he carried on his shoulders. Her knees grew weak. With a grunt and squash of caving lungs, Pierre Baptiste sprawled before her. The man he had carried rolled to her feet. It was M'sieu' Jim! A second's investigation told her he still lived.

Marcette lost all track of time. She did not see Pierre return minutes later with Nafferton, or notice his efforts to restore him. Fiery whiskey she poured down Stannard's throat. Bitterly strong tea she forced on him. She placed hot stones at his feet. Unendingly she rubbed his icy hands. She felt the heart quicken. His breathing grew more regular. He slept then, but it was not the sleep of a man freezing to death.

Pale morning frowned before he awoke. Life was all at odds and ends for Stannard. He fancied he heard again the voice of little Marcette. He was so warm and comfortable that he dreaded opening his eyes.

He remembered the storm — Nafferton — the mad Jean Cour. And then came recollection of the warm snow. He knew if he awakened from this pleasant dream, he would find himself buried there in the snow.

Someone called him. He refused to answer. Somebody shook him gently.

He opened his eyes then. Had he been dreaming? He shut and opened them again, but the girl beside him did not vanish. It was little French Marcette.

They were looking into each other's eyes. The hint of a smile hovered about the corners of Jim's cracked and bleeding mouth.

"It is you?"

"But, yes, M'sieu' Jim! Will you take just one more little drink?"

Over the rim of the tin cup, he eyed her curiously. A calm world, immaculate and imperturbable, lay beyond them. The storm had battered itself to pieces.

"What became of Nafferton and Jean Cour?" he asked.

"Pierre Baptiste cares for him, M'sieu'. He is much injured by the frost bite. Jean Cour is dead."

So the blowhard was gone. Jim shuddered at a fate he knew narrowly missed being his own.

68

"I might have known. Your coming was opportune, wasn't it, eh?" There was the suggestion of a sneer in his voice. It was for himself and his companions for failing under difficulties a frail woman had surmounted.

He saw Marcette's mouth droop and knew she had misunderstood his tone. "You're very brave. It was a terrible risk to take!"

"We travel light. We have the very best dogs. I told you at Roubideaux that Pierre knows the short trails." She paused. "He is the brave one."

She hung her head and avoided the Englishman's eyes.

Jim held her hand. "Without your urging, he would not have come," he said. "You saved my life! You know that, of course."

"But no, M'sieu' Jim! You are strong. You would have reached the Post after the storm. You will go there now? You need a long rest. Then you start out again."

Stannard knew she had lied. To a certainty he would be dead along with Jean Cour this minute but for her.

The fight she had made for him roused the best of his manhood. He laughed as he thought of Cecilie under like conditions. He must prove himself worth the battle they had made. He could not turn back.

Marcette read his thought.

"But you are not going — on?" she cried. "Windigo Creek is far away and hard to reach."

"Let me have Pierre Baptiste," Jim answered, "and I'll go on."

CHAPTER
TEN

Fool's Gold

Windigo Creek is like hundreds of others that, the ice grip removed, hurry down through the summer to join the Nishnibottni. Nor could the casual stranger in that region distinguish one from the other. They all looked alike.

"Dey are alak'." Pierre assured Stannard. "Verree much alak'. De same rock on dem; de same tree! Dey sing de same song! You hear him, M'sieu'?"

Jim was leaning against the dug-out. He shook his head as he studied the piece of quartz in his hand.

"Ah, M'sieu', you work too hard to hear de song! You t'ink you work always when de sun shine. In dees countree dee sun shin mos' all de tam' for six month straight. Don't forget dat."

"I'm not likely to forget it if I ever escape from it."

Months had elapsed since that morning among the lodge-pole pines in Jacquard's Pass. The gold lure had tempted Pierre to throw in his lot with the Englishman. The hard work of the Post was about over. Père Vallois would rave and berate him for a no-good for a day, and then buckle in and do the trader's work himself.

Nafferton had had enough of the Windigo. A strange perversity had urged him that far. His interest in wanting to know if Stannard's property was of any value can be understood. That he should know it in time was also of great importance to him. But not of such dire need as to force him to risk another adventure such as he had come through.

In a pitiable condition they had placed him in the sled behind Marcette. Three days they had waited at Jacquard's cabin for the Cree to recover strength enough to get them back to the Post. Stannard and Pierre had headed for the North then.

Days passed as they had edged for the Pole. A thaw and a freeze had crusted the snow. Miles had intervened between breakfast and the glow of their evening fire. Jim had marveled at the big Frenchman's knowledge of the untracked wilderness.

Warm days came then. Wild ducks, mallards and red heads swung by them. The creeks rose to the size of rivers. On the almost-green hillside they caught sight of a big brown bear and her fully grown cubs.

Sweet and resinous the air became with the pungent odor of cedar. It was no longer necessary to keep the night-fire booming.

The white land, which had been a place of silence, now became a garrulous, chattering Eden where wood squirrels barked all day long and magpies sauced back at them.

Pierre's heart sang. As the days grew longer, so his smile grew wider. Not so Stannard. Months were slipping by and the precious gold he had come for was

71

still as far away as ever. His discontent communicated itself to the man beside him. But how could anyone want to be elsewhere, when the whole North was smiling?

"You would leave de beautiful Nort', M'sieu'," Pierre asked incredulously. "You would go to de town where so many people be? An' de t'eatre and salon? An' women? You miss de beautiful women, eh?"

He paused as Jim continued to hack off pieces of the ore sample. Pierre smoked in silence as he conjured in his brain a picture of the future. Countless tales of the North he had told Stannard, and the Englishman had a keen respect for his philosophy.

"Women! *Voila!* You will lissen to de song of many women, M'sieu', for you will have much gold to buy de song — an' den you will regret."

He pronounced it like a prophecy.

"Dees great wide lan' wit' de win' kissin' eets way across your face, ees de only mistress. Nevaire unfaithful! Nevaire hidin' a frown of bad luck behin' a lyin' smile. *Non — non!* Dees lan' be always de same. Nevaire too much — nevaire not enough! Jus' wat you lak', no more, no less."

Subconsciously Stannard saw the sun-glow glinting the tips of the giant firs as evening shadows filled the valley before him. The smoke from their fire drifted lazily to the heavens.

Pierre picked up the piece of rock Jim had dropped. He turned it over and over in his hands.

"Dat will give you everyt'ing you wish some day." Pierre tossed the quartz to Jim's feet. "*Oui!* But eet will bring much trouble." He answered himself with a grave nod of his head. "Eet will give all t'ings to you, M'sieu' — everyt'ing but de satisfied heart."

Jim smiled. His thoughts were in London. He was back in its fogs. How he loved those fogs, just because they were English fogs. How he longed to ride again on the jerky, uncomfortable buses. He heard again the soft swish of silk. Suave, well-booted, exquisitely gowned women, grouped themselves about old drawing-rooms. Old friends greeted him. Every one there was beyond the need of anxiety, or possible failure to satisfy the appetites. Crops might face disaster; exchanges close; ships sink; mines refuse to yield; but these people — these lords and ladies of high estate — would go on smiling, chatting, eating, drinking.

Cecilie was of them. He had been. He sighed. He pitied Pierre the impulses to wean him from what was the very breath of his nostrils.

"You think this will save the day?" He asked as he toyed with the ragged ore samples.

"Eet will lose de real day! But eet will make you reech. Where dat come from much gold be."

From the dug-out Jim brought another sample. With his hand pick he broke off enough of each to give him a new face on both.

"They don't appear to be the same," he said, holding the two pieces together. "This new bit is a — a —"

"Verree old. De piece you bring from England ees of de late, hot-water tam' on de eart'. When de gold ees t'in lak' de water heemself. By'm-bye de water all dry up and leave leetle trace of gold in all dose cracks. But,

73

believe me, dees piece you bring in to-day is from de true vein. From de gold chimley eetself. Find dat vein and you have all de gold you wan'."

Pierre's geology was correct. The finding of the chimney, or fissure, by which the hot metal has come from the very bowels of the earth has always been the dream of the prospector in a hard rock country.

Began in earnest, then, a search that knew no let up. The sun grew high. Summer came and saw two men toiling like ants as they crawled and drilled their way about the Windigo. Swarms of flies came to drive them mad. Jim grew brown and strong. His hands, once so soft, were callous-hard now.

Pierre taught him how to cook, to shoot, to read sign. In the cooler evening he taught him how to fight. Not the *coup-au-pied* of the lumberjack, but the stand-up-and-hit kind of fighting, that Pierre had been fed on since boyhood.

Three times during the long months they had hailed canoes shooting down the river to faraway Roubideaux. They were from Pointe aux Barques. Once, in late August, Père Vallois sent them mail by the returning voyageurs.

There had been letters from home. The one from Cecilie was thoroughly unsatisfactory to Jim. She saw this torment he had put upon himself as a vacation, something to be endured, or put off at will.

Pierre read sign on him as correctly as he did on his woods and rivers. He remembered the night he told Marcette that only a woman could have put that look in the eyes of a man. It was true, then! He tossed the little note Marcette had written him, but which had more of Jim than of himself in it, into the fire.

He doubted that a word had ever passed between them. But he knew the way of the women of his race. In silence more than one had nursed their romances for a lifetime; unhappy but faithful and unchanging as the wild itself. How was his little girl going to be spared the unhappiness he knew was in store for her?

Cecilie's letter caused Jim to take stock of himself. Day after day for months he had toiled and sweated, sharpening drills, holding them, swinging the heavy sledges side by side with the mighty Pierre Baptiste. No word of protest had escaped his lips.

Black failure was staring at them. Even Pierre had begun to grow impatient. If ever Jim had needed an encouraging word, it was now. With trembling hands, he had opened Cecilie's letter. Its contents left him cold, sullen. He tried to make excuses for her lack of feeling; her superciliousness.

It was not self-pity that engulfed him. He had tried, — harder than he had given anyone reason to suppose he would. Faith in him was, at least in part, his earned reward. As he re-read the letter before he consigned it to the flames, he understood fully the thousands of miles they had traveled apart in the last six months.

He waited until the following day to open Diana's letter. It was an ordeal he dreaded. He knew her need of funds must be urgent. That she had in any way learned to hate this land any the less, was not to be expected.

75

He brooded all day long. Where was the way out? Diana wrote that Nafferton was still at the Post. Nafferton? — Jim knew Jean Cour had read him rightly. A lily pad! And yet he got by. Work evidently was not the certain road to existence.

Pierre tried to buck him up. The Frenchman knew a change of scene or thought, a new hope of some sort, was necessary.

So time after time that afternoon Pierre paced the angles of the fault. His studious application to whatever he had in his mind finally caught Jim's attention, even as the fascination of breaking waves holds one because of their constant repetition.

Stannard saw Pierre step off the mile and the eighth from the confluence of the creek and the river. Without a word, he turned and retraced his steps to do the same thing over. Jim had studied those lost location notices mighty well before they turned up missing. He knew that Pierre was marking them off again. But they had done this a hundred times already.

The Frenchman returned then, puffing and panting with excitement. It was acting of the first class.

"Strike me dead, by Gar! For two, t'ree week, I be t'ink and t'ink all de tam' while we drive dose drill, but I don' say not'ing. *Mon jee*, I know I foun' sumt'ing!"

He mopped his perspiring face. Jim was roused in spite of himself. "Are you fooling?" he cried, "or do you mean it? For God's sake what is it?"

"De vein!" he stuttered. "She's on de hudder side of de creek! I guess we just two dam' fool, spend all dees tam' lookin' here. De dip of de hill ought to tell us dat.

76

For why we no t'ink of dat? Ba gee, to-morrow morning we move!"

It was a blind guess on Pierre's part. It was a distraction for Jim, anyhow. It was Pierre Baptiste's turn for surprise when Jim began to find traces. He became as eager and impatient as the man he had tried to fool. Diligently they searched and pecked and drilled. Like misers they used their powder.

Their hunt became now a game of endurance. Wherever they tried they could find a color. When, after many attempts, they seemed to be on the right track, the ledge they were working would pinch out. Next week they would open another vein and always the color, sometimes faint, would be there.

It was like a grotesque game of hare and hounds. Food was temptingly held before them, but when they reached for the first mouthful it was whisked away.

The rays of the sun shot over the rim of the world and began their southern journey. Into their dug-out came the first hint of the long, cold night that holds the Arctic region by the throat.

Stannard's heart sank. But it was not the cold, clammy horror he had felt in August. Hope had been dead then. Now it was to be a fight to stick it out.

He saw the flour sack grow anæmic. The bean bag swung lightly from its hook. The geese were flying south already. Their mournful honk sent a shiver to his soul. Were they to be denied now that they were so close to their goal?

The next morning Pierre found ice in the backwaters of the creek. Time now for getting out. They held a consultation.

Jim would not listen to Pierre's plea to go out for the winter.

"But w'at we do when de snow comes? She'll be five, six feet deep in dese creek bottoms. An' col'! *Mon Dieu!* We'll freeze to deat'."

"We won't freeze, *mon ami*. By the time you get back, I'll have the dug-out sodded and plastered well enough to withstand all the cold. We've got timber to hand as we need it. I'll have a full month to run down this damn phantom before you return. If I'm lucky we can get a shaft down deep enough to drift, before the real freeze is on."

Pierre shook his head. He was not convinced. He had not spent a full winter away from Roubideaux in ten years. He longed for its gayeties in quite the same manner that Jim longed for London.

"I'll stick it out by myself if I have to, provided you find some way to get food back to me. Maybe someone will be passing for Pointe Aux Barques."

Pierre glared at him.

"Since when you get so strong dat Pierre Baptiste hav' to stay behin', eh? By Gar, dough, I goin' mees all dose dance. Well, you write some letter and I go to-morrow!"

Jim smiled but he held his head so the stalwart Pierre did not see the mist in his eyes.

That night he wrote his letters. Three attempts left an awkward note for Cecilie. He went to some length instructing Diana what to do. A draft, the last payment on his furnishings, must have been waiting him at the Post for some time. He instructed Diana to cash it, and hand half of it to Pierre to purchase their supplies.

In the early morning Pierre Baptiste swung his sturdy canoe into the swift-flowing Nishnibottni. The current caught it and so began the long voyage to the Post. Three days and nights would see him there. No such speed would mark the toiling return.

He stood up in the light canoe, a daring feat in that current, and waved his paddle at the solitary figure on the bank.

"Good-a-bye Jim," he shouted.

It was the first time he had used the Christian name between them. It thrilled the sophisticated Jim.

"*Au revoir, mon ami!*" he called to the man in the dancing canoe.

Another second and he would be out of hearing. Jim watched him speed away, he pictured the landing at the Post, three hundred miles away as the wild geese fly. He wondered who would be there to meet Pierre. Marcette? Yes, she would be there. Jim had not forgotten that she had dared a great deal for him. He remembered her croony little sing-song voice.

Pierre still saw him. There was time. He cupped his hand to his mouth and cried "Marcette — every good wish for Marcette."

The man in the canoe sat down then. It was as if he had waited for that. An instant and he was gone. Stannard was alone.

CHAPTER
ELEVEN

Suspended Payment

While the sun, that Jim and Pierre watched with varying degrees of dread, began to send down its rays athwart the Southern Cross, Nafferton hobbled about Roubideaux on his crutches, Diana always close at hand. To the English girl with her longing for home aroused by the remittance man's flair for the things which she knew and loved, the summer had brought new cares.

Marcette watched her friend's face with something approaching dismay. The simple child of nature sensed the tragedy that lay back of the tired eyes, telling of sleepless nights.

Nafferton was one source of Diana's anxiety. With patience born of experience, he had broken through the wall of reserve with which she had surrounded herself. With Jim absent, the remittance man had a free hand. Nor did he hesitate to take advantage of the opportunities her lack of finances afforded him.

Lonesomeness was his chief ally. Lonesomeness and the silence and fear of the unknown.

The open spaces sent a shiver down the sensitive spine of the English girl. She demanded the shelter of four walls. She needed to know that there was some male of the species ready at hand to battle against nature for her, to provide, to cherish, to protect.

Her brother was away out there, in the biting North. Pierre was with him. Only Marcette and Père Vallois stood between Nafferton and her affections. These two afforded her only passing solace, and no permanent refuge.

Diana was famished; mad for excitement; worrying herself to the point of hysteria, for want of diversion.

Nafferton filled that want.

The draft which Jim expected had not come. She was dependent on Nafferton to meet the fixed charges of life, which in the North are great indeed for one who must have some of the luxuries she has been acustomed to, as a balance against the monotonously rough fare of the Post.

It was not with a light tone that Diana approached the question of the delayed draft for the tenth time.

"It's all right, Diana," Nafferton replied with an all too familiar air. "Don't worry about the bally thing. I still have a few dollars, y'know."

With a generous sweep of his hand, that his heart belied, he crushed a bill between her fingers.

"How can I ever repay you?"

There was sincerity in Diana's question. She feared the outcome of Jim's battle. She feared the delay of the draft. She feared the approaching winter with its long night and the cry of the wolf pack echoing against the hills.

"My dear, that's easy." And to prove that he meant what he said, he kissed her affectionately. For an instant she clung to him.

The strong, pliant fingers of nature stripped away their artificialities. They looked upon one another with the bewildering frankness Adam and Eve had felt in the Garden of Eden.

Nafferton kissed her again and they went down the trail toward the Fort.

Marcette wondered. She had seen the kiss, but not the incident which prompted it.

There was something unclean about the man that turned her blood cold. She wished Jim were there. No good could come of this. She recalled the night Pierre and she had marked him for a rotter.

She sat on the steps of the Fort, moody and glum. She sensed unhappiness for Jim in Nafferton's fondness for Diana. It grew cold. She arose to enter the building, when a speck dancing down the river caught her eye. A minute and there came to her the song of a riverman. She knew the song by heart. It was the *Chanson du Rossignol*. Pierre had taught it to her in childhood, and whistled the call of the little Rossignol as she sang.

The figure grew until it became familiar. With a shout, Marcette recognized him. Fast as she ran, he was at the landing before her. With a mighty swing he bore her aloft and carried her protestingly to old André's doorstep.

Père Vallois rushed forward to meet them and only remembered by the barest fraction of time, that Pierre was in for a lesson. No man could come and go with the affairs of the North West Company in the manner Pierre Baptiste had employed that Spring.

"So you come home, eh?" André flung at him.

"Yes, I come home all right, but by Gar, I turn right 'round an' go back in two, t'ree day. We know dees English are all dam' fools; but dis Jim ees de worst of all. Not'ing I say mak' heem come away. Dat fool goin' to stay up dere all wintaire and me, I got to stay dere wit' heem."

"You call him Jim?" Marcette questioned. Her voice was pitched low. There was a modulation to it, new to the ears of Pierre. He turned on her, so marked was the change in her voice and manner.

"Wat you do, Marcette? What happen in five, six little month mak' you change so? She ees change' eh, Père Vallois?"

The Factor was non-committal.

"Marcette grow much, that is all. But change? No."

Pierre edged close to her.

"Jim say before I leave, 'Best wish for Marcette.'"

A blush mounted the delicate cheek of the girl.

"What did he say for M'sieu' Nafferton, with the frozen feet?" Père Vallois asked sarcastically.

"He was badly frozen," Marcette interposed. "Even now he walk so." She limped across the floor, the better to hide her own embarrassment at Jim's message. "He does it too well to make believe," she continued.

"Jim say not'ing about Nafferton, but I hav' beeg lettaire for Ma'm'selle. We go see her now, eh, Marcette?"

Through the dusk they walked to Diana's cabin. If Pierre hid his surprise at the change in the English girl, it was only because he possessed a quality she would not have given him credit for.

He remembered her proud and imperious. Some of her beauty of body was gone. She was thinner. The eagerness with which she asked for word of her brother was his greatest surprise.

Diana had seen them approaching. She had, of course, recognized Pierre and the fact that he was alone smote her. Had Jim returned with him he would have been to see her before now. Was more bad news, further misery to be visited upon her, she asked. For weeks Marcette had said the two of them would be returning any day. What could have held Jim back? Sickness? Or death? She knew men did die out there to the North.

Although Diana had told herself every day that Jim would not succeed in his venture, nevertheless she had hoped against hope that he might win out on that hundredth chance she allowed him. Her urgent need of money forced her to build on the thought. She dreaded to think of the future unless he did win. She liked Nafferton. Too well, she admitted. She was in his debt for a huge sum already.

Then, like a bomb, the idea struck her that maybe Jim had hit it and had sent Pierre with the news. She actually trembled with the thought.

Pierre's story brought a cold perspiration to her brow. Her misery and humbleness touched the heart of the giant. For the first time he saw her as a human being.

In silence Marcette and Pierre traced their way back to the Fort. Marcette had wanted to tell Pierre about the affair with Nafferton and ask his advice; but the Frenchman's dismay at the non-arrival of the draft made her change her mind.

Pierre had no appetite for his supper that night. Without money, what was he to do? Would Nafferton come to Jim's rescue? He doubted it. He had nothing but contempt for the remittance man, who never by any chance received a remittance. Still it was a hope.

Marcette's eyes followed him as he walked to the door.

"I go see dis M'sieu' Nafferton. We have sumt'ing to talk 'bout for sure."

The girl wondered just what Pierre had found to talk to him about. She drew in her breath sharply. Had he in some way suspected what was going on at Roubideaux?

CHAPTER
TWELVE

Le Chat Civet

It was some time before Nafferton opened the door. The sensitive ear of the Frenchman heard the tread of a light foot on the planks. When he stood on the threshold responding to Nafferton's greeting his nostrils caught a delicate perfume.

Pierre had wandered about the Post for an hour trying to outline the request he had to make. The faint fragrance of that dainty perfume sent his thoughts tumbling.

The English run to strange ways in the North, according to the natives. But Nafferton had been long enough in the country to have outgrown most of them; especially *"Le Chat Civet!"* That sweetener of the imagination was too dainty, too feminine to hold out long on the upper Nishnibottni. Pierre remembered the light footsteps and glanced at Nafferton's heavy boot and the crippled foot in its soft Mackinaw felt.

Nafferton had learned soon after Pierre's visit to Diana that he was in the Post, and that Jim was not with him. He was anxious for exact information about the mine.

"Oh, we get heem soon, M'sieu'," Pierre informed him. "Every day we find de color. Somewhere we run into de pay-chute, an' den, *voila*, we bot' be millionaire."

"You really think it is as good as that, eh? Just a case of running it down?"

"I always spik de trut' M'sieu'." Pierre cocked his eye at him. "Too bad you don't have some claim dere yourself."

Nafferton wondered just what prompted that remark.

He heard Pierre unfold his plan to have him lend him the money Jim needed. He smiled. Things were playing right into his hands. If the property looked this good it was marketable. And at a price! If Jim were forced to let it go because of lack of funds to keep up his work it would be easier than he had suspected.

He gave Pierre a dozen reasons why it was impossible for him to advance the money. His solicitation for Jim sounded overdone to the Frenchman.

Money, or no money, Nafferton knew it would be a question now if Jim could get out in time to save his neck. Snow was possible any day.

Pierre argued with patience. Nafferton wondered if he would never go. He was uneasy. The big fellow caught Nafferton's eye as it strayed to the heavy blanket that partitioned off an end of the room. He thought he saw it move.

So, that was where the fragrant odor of *"Le Chat Civet!"* came from. "She's behin' dat *arras*, eh,

M'sieu," he said to himself. *"Une petite belle!* But who?"

The perfume seemed to grow in strength as he continued to stare at the blanket. Pierre at least could enjoy Nafferton's uneasiness. He heard him express for the hundredth time his regret that he could not help Jim. Always it was the same with these English. "My remittance is overdue."

Pierre Baptiste had once essayed a song to the refrain:

"My remittance is much overdue,
How-do-you-do? How-do-you-do?"

Insolently he stood at the door and gazed at the blanket. He knew it moved then. He had a parting shot for Nafferton. "Nobody find out who stole Jim's money yet, eh? We catch heem some day."

Nafferton shuddered as Pierre's laugh came back to him. Why was it that an ignorant brute like the big Frenchman could make him feel so cheap and small? They would never catch *him!*

Unconsciously he stroked his jugular vein between his thumb and forefinger. "God!" he muttered to himself. "He could tear a man's throat apart with those hands."

A girl's voice whispered, "Has he gone?"

Nafferton turned from his gloomy picture to the pleasures that were at hand.

The lights in La Pointe's place had beckoned to Pierre. He wandered into the smoky bar-room. Ritchie was there, back from the Misstassini. A few others, also, whom he did not know — men, who had come in already from their summer with the pick and drill.

They hailed Pierre with delight. He heard their tales with interest, but was glum himself. Jim had begged him not to talk. Things had taken such a bad turn since his arrival that the admonition was unnecessary.

Pichon, the one-eared octogenarian of the Post, scraped his fiddle. Good whiskey and old Pichon's music had thrilled Pierre many times in the past. He watched as the dancing grew wilder, and the singing violin raised its voice. It did not call to him to-night. He wanted to be alone.

He wandered back to the trade-room at the Post. He tried to concentrate on the disaster facing Jim, but the memory of *"Le Chat Civet!"* obtruded time and again.

It was intensified when the door opened and Marcette entered. For she brought in her hair an intangible reminder of the perfume he had smelled that night in Nafferton's cabin.

He stared at her until his eyes popped. Had it been Marcette, who had hidden behind the blanket? The thought seered his soul.

The look in his eyes frightened her. Père Vallois called her as she started to speak. Pierre thanked high Heaven for that. He wanted to get outside and think.

When Marcette returned she was surprised to find him gone. She would have been more astonished if she could have seen him trailing her footprints in the heavy frost.

Straight for Nafferton's cabin they carried him. But as the realization of the fact grew on him, they turned and right-angled to Diana's cabin. He quartered every foot of ground, but could not find where they had crossed to Nafferton's place. He back-trailed them, then, to the Post door.

He drew a sigh of relief. Silently he stole to his old room but hours slipped by before sleep came, his mind was busy with thoughts of Marcette.

The timbers of the Post, cracking aloud as the early sun drew the frost out of them, awakened him. The night had been unusually cold for that time of year. He made his simple toilet hurriedly. The fusillade of the snapping logs made him wince. It brought poignantly to mind the picture of Jim waiting for the badly needed provisions.

The incident of the night before, with its crucifying suspicion of Marcette, had dulled his faculties to the urgency of Jim's need. Over and over again he called himself worse than a fool for harboring a doubt of the child he had helped to raise. The thought was ugly, unworthy of her.

Everything had gone wrong since he had arrived at the Post. He fancied he caught in Père Vallois' manner a coolness, a lack of that old-time *cameraderie*. It was unlike the old man to carry a grudge. He could not believe it was entirely due to the happy-go-lucky way in which he had severed his connection with the Company last Spring. Pierre knew the Factor's hatred of this gold craze, which boded ill for the North West posts.

With all of his crudeness and rough ways, Pierre had the sensitiveness of a child. It is a racial trait hard to overcome. It made him read in André's early morning greeting a reserve that killed any thought of appealing to him for credit. Pierre knew the rules of the company as well as the Factor. He had made himself an outsider by throwing up his job. Any supplies given to him now would be on a purely personal basis. He knew the old man to be a stickler for the laws made at Cumberland House. Under happier circumstances he would not have hesitated to ask for aid even so; but he could not risk the embarrassment of a refusal now.

He was Jim's messenger, and beyond the question of supplies for the mine, he knew he had to make some arrangement for his friend's sister against the time when the expected draft should arrive.

He wanted to talk it over with Marcette, but even there he felt stopped. An insensate hatred of Nafferton filled him. His fists clenched as he saw him hobble across the compound. He would have liked to have thrown him, crutches and all, into the moaning river.

All morning long he sulked in the sunny shelter of the wharf. The dropping of many pebbles on his drowsy head caused him to look up. His quick eye caught the laughing face of Marcette as it drew back over the top of the landing. Another second and she squatted in the sand beside him.

Pierre gazed longingly at her and felt the suspicion of the night before flying away. Those widely set, straightly level eyes of hers were too frank, too innocent, to allow doubt to remain.

The big man smiled then until his lips parted and his white teeth gleamed. Marcette forced her little hand into his. She smiled too.

"Why so blue and cross, Pierre?" she asked, her forehead puckering into a quizzical frown.

Pierre laughed aloud at that. It was good to be able to tell her.

"Blue? You ask me why I'm so blue, *ma petite?* Bagosh, you hear last night dat monee not come for Jim. What I goin' to do? We need all dose t'ings to eat; powdaire; clothes! Even if I get dem what I goin' do here wit'out no monee, *Mon Dieu!* He come on de run, eef I leave his sistaire hungry."

"Well, *mon père,* he do something for you!"

"*Non, non,* Marcette, dat ole man hee's cross lak' a bear. I know what he say about de Nort' West rule, even 'fore he say eet."

"Then I'll ask him for you. I never thought you would turn out such a coward."

Marcette arose and brushed the sand from her skirt, ready to put her words into action.

"Ees dat so? Well you bes' not ask heem. He snap your head off."

Père Vallois suspected the mission that brought Marcette into the big trade-room. He knew by heart the wiles that preceded the asking of an unusual favor.

Marcette did not get far. "And Pierre he ask me —"

The old Factor banged his hand on the heavy counter. "Pierre!" he chortled. "That fool he ask you to ask for him? Why does he not ask himself? Because he knows what my answer would be. First he runs away and leaves me to make out as I can. Then he works his hands off chasing fool gold, which, if found, would turn this Post into a mad-house."

"But, he do many things in the past for the Nor' West Company. That ought to make some difference."

"It make no difference to me. For fifteen years I treat that fool like he was a son to me. What has this Englishman Jim ever done for him? Still he break his neck for that man. Trouble, trouble — everywhere these English come there's trouble. First he lose his money; then you scare me to death trying to save him from the very thing we all warned him against. Did he once come to me for advice? No. *Mon Dieu*, if they can't come to me for advice they can't come to me begging for help."

Marcette stamped her little foot. She was her father's daughter. It took all of her strength to swing the heavy door of the room; but she threw it shut now, with a bang.

"I never expected to live to hear a Vallois go back on a friend," she cried from the steps.

It made her father both wince and smile.

CHAPTER
THIRTEEN

A Man Shall Die

Marcette was so crestfallen that Pierre laughed, although from her manner he knew the answer she had received.

There was life on the river. The Fox River Nascaupees were going down stream, their canoes well loaded with provisions for the winter ahead. More than once he had given them their allowance. Some of them had credits of three and four hundred counters with the North West Company.

There was fascination in watching the quickly moving waters. It was the railroad of the North. To its tune, life ebbed and flowed.

The minutes dragged by. It was fairly warm in the shelter of the landing. Conversation lagged, but the minds of both were busy. Nemiskau, majestic in his old age, strode to where they sat. With the quiet dignity of his race, he squatted beside them.

The trivialities of life had no concern with him. To the unknowing, no thought hung on the brow of the Nascaupee. Marcette watched him. His very inaction told her he was not at ease. Pierre caught the silent play of watcher and watched. He became a player, too.

94

The stage was set for the Indian. From his waist he unhooked a well-oiled trap. He tossed it to Pierre's feet.

Pierre reached for it and turned it over in his hand.

It was in excellent condition and, by the smell of it, only lately oiled. He set the spring, and then sprang it with a stick. Nemiskau's features did not change. Evidently he had not brought it to be fixed. Pierre turned inquiringly to Marcette.

The old Indian pointed to the disappearing canoes.

Marcette uttered a cry of understanding.

"Don't you see, thick one, what he means? The trap is your own. He means for you to take your traps to the Windigo. What Factor of either company would refuse credit to you, running a line?"

Nemiskau smiled. They understood.

Pierre's grin came back with a leap.

"See," he beamed, "some folks lak' dis Nafferton call dat Injun dam' fool. He's twice more smart than any of us."

Old André could not go back on Pierre's argument now. But he bedeviled him as Pierre had never dreamed a man could.

Of course what Pierre did not know was that Père Vallois had given the trap to the Indian.

Before the Frenchman left a hundred counters were placed to Diana's credit. Ample to see her through until the draft did arrive, provided she was careful of them.

Pierre viewed with alarm the well-filled dunnage bags. Into his own duffel he placed a package for M'sieu' Jim. More than once he would have to use the tumpline before he reached home. Leg-weary leagues of portage faced him. Ice was in the river. Night travel would be too dangerous.

Day after day, though, he won back the miles. The babiche thong cut into his head some days for hours at a time.

It was not adventure to Pierre. Just hard, grinding, back-breaking work, the like of which he had known a thousand times.

The creeks appeared then. Another day and he turned up the Windigo. It was frozen from bank to bank. His wild halloo brought Jim on the double-quick.

The fire roared that night in the little dug-out. The wilds make men taciturn, quiet and slow of speech. That is in fiction. Not so in the flesh. To-night was Christmas Eve, New Year's, the Fourth of July, all rolled into one for Jim Stannard.

There was good news and bad news for him. Jim's anxiety for Diana was keen. Pierre wisely kept his suspicions of Nafferton under cover. Stannard smiled at Pierre's description of the change his sister had wrought in Marcette. He fumbled with the exquisite pouch and its accompanying store of excellent tobacco which she had sent him. She was a thoughtful little beggar. He wondered if Pierre would rise to the heights with her. He knew the way of women when they get the ambition to climb.

The matter of the traps elicited a good laugh. It had been a life saver. Of Nafferton, Jim was only mildly curious. The meagre mail held no letter from Cecilie. It would be April before he could hear from her or get a letter out. Close to a year would have elapsed between times. Too long for a girl to wait for a man thousands of miles away.

Jim was well down in the barren quartz before Pierre's return. The start was promising enough to buoy them up. By the time winter had set in in earnest they were well down below the frost line.

Pierre ran his traps mornings and worked the prospect in the short hours of afternoon.

He got his share of fox and mink and an occasional marten. The caribou were drifting, and he kept the camp well supplied with meat. But Jim stuck religiously to his task — five, six, even seven hours a day, as the light held.

Pierre knew they were down far enough to be getting results.

"When you goin' cross-cut de vein?" he asked seriously.

"We won't cross-cut it," Jim replied. "I'm going to drift on the fifty-foot level. If I can't find the pay-chute on the surface I'll hunt for it underground."

There was an air of finality to Jim's talk that made the Frenchman smile.

When the winter storms hurled themselves against the rim of the Copper Kettle, the two men worked in the sheltered shaft. On clear days they operated the windlass and removed the gangue of previous days. They ran into sugarloaf quartz. Their progress became more rapid.

One day Pierre thought he heard Jim whistle a bar or two of a song. He looked up quickly.

"What you foun'?" he cried excitedly.

"Nothing. Only we're getting down now. We can begin to drift any time."

Pierre was the last out of the shaft that night. He noticed his feet were wet. His mouth tightened a trifle and he shook his head.

The next morning when Jim slid down the footwall, holding on to the windlass rope, to keep himself from a too precipitous descent, he landed in water to his knees.

"The snow has drifted in," he called up to Pierre. "There's two feet of water in the shaft."

Pierre swung down beside him. He swore voluminously.

"We'll have to bank these logs on top. We can't work in this flood."

The Frenchman hated to tell him the truth.

"Eet ees not de snow, Jim. We're down below the water level. Get out of here P D Q or we get de rheumatiz for keep."

They were stopped now without hope of going on. For two days Jim lay in his bunk staring at the smoky ceiling, trying to conjure some way out of their difficulty.

"Dat last shot of mine do eet," Pierre growled. "When I come up dat night my feet were wet. But I don't say not'ing."

"That was three days ago?" Jim asked. "That water has not risen an inch since yesterday morning. It may have reached its level now and not rise until the spring thaws come."

"I guess you may be right. But why you ask?"

Jim sat up.

"Pierre, did you ever hear of a sump?"

It was new to the Frenchman. It was a tool he had never heard of.

"A sump?" he asked incredulously. "Wat ees dis sump? Where we goin' get heem?"

Jim laughed. "We've got one already. All we need is to put it to work."

He then explained to Pierre what a sump was. It is really only a platform built above the water in a shaft. Provided the water remains stationary, it is possible to build such a device and run a tunnel above it.

"We are down as far as we want to go anyway. I believe it's all luck from now on. I'll match you to see whether we drift north or south. Heads or tails?"

"Heads," shouted Pierre, entering into the spirit of the gamble.

"Tails it is. We'll drift north."

Pierre cooked their meagre supper. Praising, turning a jest, meeting every handicap with a smile, he had gone on, humoring the other man, trying by every subterfuge to keep his interests alive.

He gazed at him sympathetically as he dried the dishes. The Englishman's grit and resourcefulness had completely won the big Frenchman.

The period of enforced idleness was over. Tomorrow they would drive above the sump and go on. When would the next rebuff come? Left to his own decision, Pierre knew he would have given it up long ago. These English had the grit.

Jim went through his handful of books. Somewhere he had read about a sump. His partner watched him through the tobacco smoke. This continuous application to work, this perpetual goading of oneself to a given task, fretted the Frenchman. He spoke aloud.

"Fonny t'ing, Jim," he said; "eet mak' me wondaire sometam' why you go on lak' dis. Work, work, all de tam'. For yourself, I say no. No man work lak' dis for heemself. For de little sistaire den? An' again I say no. Even for her you don't go on. *Cherchez la femme!* For one little woman, dat's eet. For her you freeze in he wintaire an' sweat when de sun and de flies come. When de snow fills up de shaf' or de water swamps eet, you go on. All for her. For her you wan' de gol'."

Jim closed his book. He stared into the fire.

"You're right, Pierre. It was for a girl I wanted the gold. Not the gold itself, but the things it would buy for the two of us. London, home, the little luxuries, it meant all that to us." He shook his head. "When it comes I am afraid it will be too late. Too late for her."

Pierre raked the coals.

"Non, non, Jim. Eet's nevaire too late for de right girl. Always you worry and fight for try to fin' dis gol'. You forget to laugh. You nevaire hear de birds when dey sing, or de win' when she play all dose little tune. Me, I laugh! I sing! When I don' feel lak' work, I don' work. Not'ing evaire worry Pierre Baptiste. I come an' I go. No one in dis worl' worry 'bout me. 'Cept maybe dat baby, Marcette. Some feller come along an' he say, 'Pierre Baptiste, how you lak' go to de Peace Rivier wid me?' Or maybe it ees de Hay or de Brulé. Dat's long trip but if I lak' to go, I go. Money? Gol'? I don' worry 'bout heem. I need little money — I trap, or hunt, or work on de Pos' for little while. Everyt'ng come out hall right jes de same. But you? All you say ees Englan'. Why you need dat Englan' so much?"

"For the same reason, Pierre, that you need these woods and hills. You would die in the big cities with their crowded streets and dirt and noise. My heart's back there. It's home. For a year I have prayed and hoped that I might strike it out here. I wanted the chance to taste a million things that had been denied me. Money will buy a lot back there."

Jim reached out for the book he had been reading. He sighed. "I wonder if I'll ever get back."

"Nothing here would hold you, eh, Jim?" A shrewd look was in Pierre's eyes.

"No. No. Home is where the heart is."

Under his breath Pierre repeated the words. Before him appeared an image of Marcette. He saw her laughing eyes. They grew sad then, and the vision faded. He wondered if in the years to come he would be able to bring back that smile.

Never once, by word or look, had he given her reason to think that the old relation between them had changed. She was a woman, even to him, now. He would have given his life to have kindled in her eyes the light Jim had placed there.

Stannard had marked his place with an old letter. He opened it and handed it to Pierre. There was a little sketch of a sump and tunnel. The Frenchman could not read, but the picture told the story. He held the book close to the lamp. The picture of the sump faded from his mind. From the letter there arose to his nostrils a memory of *"Le Chat Civet!"* He sniffed it again.

"You lak' dat smell, Jim?" he asked, handing the opened book and letter to Stannard.

"Enticing — what?"

"Dat little girl back home, she lak' *'Le Chat Civet!'* eh?"

Jim laughed. "No. No. That's the note from Marcette — the one you brought."

Pierre snatched the letter away from him. "No," he cried. "I guess you mak' meestak'."

"Don't be ridiculous. Here, give it to me and I'll read it to you again. But why so curious? What the devil difference does it make?"

"Where Marcette get dat perfume?" Pierre demanded. "Perhaps Ma'm'selle bring eet to de Pos'?"

"Absolutely no. It is not used in England. Its fragrance never dies. Place a handkerchief sprinkled with it in a room, and its bouquet will settle into everything there."

Pierre saw red. Murder surged in his heart. In spite of all his convictions to the contrary had Marcette been in Nafferton's cabin?

Spring could not come soon enough now.

Jim was speaking: "My friend Nafferton had a *penchant* for it. He might have given it to Marcette."

At the sound of that name Pierre jumped. His white face frightened Stannard.

"You hear me now, Jim. Some day I'm goin' keel your frien' Nafferton. Don' ask me why. Wait! Let me fin' out two, t'ree t'ing, dat's all. An' den, *voila*, I keel heem jes lak' dat!" And in his mighty hand Pierre Baptiste crushed to a pulp the cup he had whipped from the table.

CHAPTER
FOURTEEN

A Promise is Broken

Nafferton did not tarry long in Roubideaux after Pierre's visit. Things were at such a pass with Diana that flight became imperative. Ritchie and the Choate boys were going out on the last boat. He knew their tales would set tongues wagging. Fools of one sort and another would be foregathering that winter at Trois Riviers. A man with a claim to sell could not afford to be elsewhere.

Diana read doom for herself in his departure. Her very life had become dependent on him. She begged him to take her. She grew haggard and careworn as the day for the departure of the boat drew near.

Nafferton had discarded his crutches for a cane. He worked himself into a frightful temper as he hobbled around his cabin. The girl's pleading fell on deaf ears. He was no hand for faded flowers.

Time after time he assured her that he would be back within the next month, or as soon as the first heavy snows of winter had become fit for travel, and that they would be married then.

Marriage was vital to Diana now. Luckily for Nafferton, Father Malotte was away from the Post at present. He would have been sorely put to it to have convinced her of the need of further delay in that respect had the priest been at home.

The sight of tears in the girl's eyes drove him frantic.

"Good God!" he cried. "Don't do that. You fret me to death. My word, why must you be eternally weeping and nagging me? You'll drive me mad."

"Mad?" She echoed his own words. "It is I, who will go mad. You know where I stand. I want you to promise me you will come back. That we will be married."

"I've told you so a dozen times."

"Ashleigh, I'll die if you don't. I could not face the world — or Jim. If Jim knew, it would kill him."

"Well, he will never know unless you tell him. I er — er — wouldn't do that. Months will go by before he comes out. We will be married then and able to do as we please."

It was the only promise she could wring from him. He sailed away with a flourish.

Shortly after his departure Diana moved into his cabin. It was larger than her own and held memories of the man she had blindly followed.

The days grew shorter and the snows came to lock the white land in silence. Marcette became a dominating factor in Diana's life. Without her things would have been impossible. The French girl's infectious laugh, her ready smile, awakened interest in Diana at a time when existence seemed a ghastly tragedy.

In return she taught Marcette how to speak, and many of the little courtesies refined people set such store by. Best of all she encouraged her to sing. There was a bird-like quality in her voice that Diana marveled at. Given the proper training, that quality alone would take a singer to the heights.

Days went on and Diana found that, unconsciously, she had planted the ambition to be a great singer in Marcette. The English girl was sorry at that. It seemed rank ingratitude to nurse an ambition into flame only to see it smothered and killed because of lack of opportunity.

January and February rolled by as Marcette sang and trilled her way about the Fort. Christmas had been a big success. Old Pichon had played to her singing and she had done well. By March she had out-distanced her teacher.

Many weeks, even months, had elapsed since Nafferton's going.

From Marcette, Diana had elicited the information that the Factor expected word from Trois Riviers that week. The snow was in fine condition and the prospect of clear weather promising. Friday, a dog-team came in. The Indian musher was alone. Nor did the mail bring any word from the man for whom she so patiently waited.

Her reaction brought on the first sinking spell. In desperation she was moved to confide her secret to Marcette — Diana was soon to be a mother. That Nafferton would return now was past believing.

Père Vallois became worried at Marcette's pale cheeks. She was strangely quiet for one who had only lately driven him frantic with her trilling and ah-ah-ing.

106

"What make you so quiet, *ma petite?*" he asked. "All day long you girls are together. What you do all that time?"

"I learn so much, *mon père*. All the time I must study and read. Diana says one cannot sing well, if they have not an education. And I teach her how to sew and make so many pretty things. And then 'fore we know it, *voila*, it's time to go to bed."

She threw her arms around his neck and pecked at his cheeks with her lips. "So you see we are busy. Are we not Daddy?"

Old André did not know whether he liked that "daddy" or not. It was too foreign. Marcette's answer had not satisfied him. There was an air of secrecy about her which he could not explain.

Through the window he saw her hurrying to Nafferton's old place. It gave him food for thought. What would be the outcome of this foolish notion of hers — this wanting to go away to become a great singer. That was bad. She was northern bred. She belonged in the North.

More than once the Factor had wondered if Pierre Baptiste would win her hand. The last year had not pointed that way. He was a fool. And she a hopeless minx. André would have held the highest none too good for her. But Pierre was her kind. He was a good man to have by. But a rolling stone! When would these young fools see that chasing rainbows brought them nowhere?

Could the grizzled Factor have peered into the shaft on the Windigo he would have pointed in scorn at the rainbow chasing going on there.

With his adze, Pierre had squared off the heavy timbers and built the platform above the water. From it they had cut into the solid rock and drifted North. Day after day they burrowed into the quartz. Forty, fifty, a hundred feet they went. Ephemeral, elusive, the yellow gold beckoned them on.

Pierre turned to his traps with relief. Success here was certain. The previous week he had brought in a silver tip. The coat was long and in excellent condition. It was a grubstake for the summer in itself.

Spring began to edge in. The days were getting longer. Two months more and he would be on his way to settle accounts with Nafferton. He nursed his hatred of him as a mother does a child.

Jim had become thin and nervous. The long grind was taking its toll. He complained of not feeling well. Pierre dosed him with the simple remedies they had to hand, ably backed up by that first and last remedy of the far North, good whiskey.

The following day when Pierre returned from his traps, he found a madman cutting and hacking at the blind lead.

"It's here! It's here!" Jim cried, his eyes staring straight ahead as if to pierce the rock that held back the ghost gold.

With an effort the Frenchman tied him in the ore bucket and pulled him to the surface.

Pierre cared for him as if he were a baby, but his fever increased. To remain there meant death for Jim. Snowshoes or the hand sled were the only means of travel. Pierre knew Jim would be dead long before they reached Roubideaux were he to try either.

Some day this month the trains from Pointe Aux Barques would be going through. He set up a signal for them at the mouth of the creek.

Two days passed and no sound came to him but the moaning of the sick man in the dug-out. The mighty Frenchman realized that the precious, life-giving days were growing few.

All of his strength and cunning availed him not. For once in his life Pierre was helpless, waiting on the whim of fate to send relief to him.

It was growing dusk. He listened intently. He had heard a shout. He opened the door and saw the dogs coming on the lope. Another half hour and they would have gone by his signal in the dark.

A minute, and Jacques La Voie stood framed in the doorway. There were three teams in the train, and while they talked the other men came up.

They cached the load of one sled in the dug-out and tenderly placed Stannard in the empty sled. Jacques left one of his Indians there and arranged to send for his own and Pierre's skins at once. Jim's partner knew that this would give him money enough to go to any length to help Stannard back to health.

To give the sick man a chance for his life meant continuous going. The snow could not have been better. The dogs could stand the driving. On Jim himself rested the outcome. His months in the open, a clean past in back of him, were to weigh for him now.

Pierre pulled in his belt as the days went by. He grew gaunt.

Black circles gathered beneath his eyes. The dogs rolled their tongues in agony at the giant who forced them on.

Pierre used every means of deduction to assure himself that Father Malotte would be at the Post. Without him the effort would be useless. The man of God was the only doctor in that vast region. On the certainty that he would be at Roubideaux, Pierre fought on.

By the Devil's Bedroom and Jacquard's cabin he cut through to Lac Ste. Jean. It was the same short cut he had used the night Marcette and he had gone to Jim's rescue a year ago. Today no storm held him back.

Noontime found him at Caribou Rocks. Night came on. In the distance, glowed the lights of the Post. Jim still lived. He would be in time.

Men left their suppers to stare out of windows, at the yelling shadow which dashed by to the door of the Fort. Père Vallois gazed with open mouth at the apparition which brushed its way past him, carrying a full-grown man in his arms.

"Get de pries' *tout' suite!*" Pierre's voice trailed back from the stairs, as he carried Jim to the room he had always called his own.

"*Tout' suite! Tout' suite!*" he called again, as the door banged shut and Jim sank into the soft feathers of the bed.

110

CHAPTER
FIFTEEN

The Coming of Little White Hair

Pierre waited for the sound of footsteps on the stairs to tell him the old priest was on the way. He had sensed the banging of the heavy outside door minutes back. Old André must have gone in search of the good Father. The inaction of waiting was too much for the Frenchman. He rushed downstairs to come face to face with the Factor returning empty-handed from his search.

"Couldn't you find heem?" he asked excitedly. "Where's he gone? He mus' come queeck. Jim die eef he don'. Night an' day we come all de way. Bagosh, we don' do dat for not'ing. Where's Marcette? She gone, too?"

"*Mon Dieu!* I don't see either one all evening. Sure, they come back soon. I'll have Aleekna get some supper. What's the matter with the Englishman?"

"Crazee as a loon wid de fever. You don' min' 'bout dat supper. I eat after while. I'm goin' fin' dat pries'."

On the run, he went off to search for him. He went to the little chapel with its tiny rectory; to La Pointe's and the other houses down that way. No one had seen the *curé* since evening.

Père Vallois gave up searching for the man of God, and went for Marcette whom he was sure he would find with Diana.

All day long the English girl had suffered the travaille that motherhood alone can bring.

It had fallen to Marcette to appraise Father Malotte of Diana's need of him. For hours, the little grey-haired man had held the hand of the strange girl and sought to bring relief to both body and soul. He was a product of a wild land, holding the sins of the flesh not too heavily against the penitent.

In her short intervals of consciousness Diana appealed to Marcette to care for her baby. The promise was given readily. The beautiful mystery of motherhood held Marcette in its spell. She could not keep back her tears.

"Promise me," murmured the stricken girl, in tones so low Marcette had to bend close to catch them, "promise me Jim will never know. And you, good father, promise me, too."

"He shall not be told, my child. Rest easy on that account. Will yourself to come through this ordeal. The Man I represent will not hold your mistake against you. But he would not forgive your failure to strive to live."

By loving kindness the little priest had worked many miracles. But his knowledge of medicine and surgery were only rudimentary. Even so, he recognized that the crisis now approached.

He sent Marcette for Aleekna and bade her to wait at the Post until he sent for her.

Aleekna came unhurriedly. Birth and death usually found her at hand. Priest and Indian did their best. But their best did not suffice. As happens all too often in the North, Diana, like many other mothers, died that her child might live.

In the dusk Aleekna came plodding home, bearing her bad news. Marcette made a pretense at eating to quiet her father's curiosity. She was sparring for time against the minute when he must be told the truth.

Father Malotte had mercifully drawn the blanket across the corner of the room in which Diana lay before Marcette entered. From a bundle of warm blankets a little blond head appeared.

Silently, the two of them knelt and prayed for the soul of the poor dead girl. Thus it was that Père Vallois and Pierre Baptiste found them. They met at the doorway. The Factor had been best pleased to have found himself alone on this errand.

Pierre had not come to Nafferton's cabin for Father Malotte. He wanted to see Nafferton. If Marcette was not to be found, elsewhere, she must be here. As he came panting to the door of the cabin Pierre knew he would kill the Englishman if he found Marcette within.

The Factor's hand was upon the lock.

"We bot' come on de same errand, eh, M'sieu'?"

Père Vallois turned on him.

"Perhaps we do. But I do my own errands, Pierre Baptiste. Don't forget that. I do not come here to find a priest."

"Nor do I, M'sieu'. I know she ees here, Marcette. For six months I have close to me a perfume I smell firs' in dis cabin. Later I smell it in her hair. It choked me. Now I — fine out 'bout dat."

His strong hand opened the door menacingly. Père Vallois was only a step behind him. Both of them froze where they stood at the sight which met their eyes — the interrupted prayer, the crying girl and the fretting baby awakened by their loud words.

No one spoke. The silence grew until the ticking of the clock on the dresser came like hammer blows. No one of them seemed willing to break the spell that held them. Pierre's pent up emotion strangled him. He coughed miserably.

Father Malotte faced them then. With a bound Marcette sprang forward to shield the baby from their prying eyes. She caught it to her, and mothered the little thing. The priest stepped in front of her his hand raised.

"Stop your senseless brawling," he fired at them. "You walk to-night in the house of death."

"Death?" André managed to gasp.

The priest beckoned them behind the blanket where Diana lay cold and white. Terror congealed in Pierre. Death was not new to him: but the unexpectedness of it, the tragedy of Jim lying at the Post dying himself made it twice as cruel.

He knelt beside his friend's dead sister to mutter a prayer. Like fire the fragrant odor of *Le Chat Civet!* burned into his nostrils.

114

Pierre came into the center of the room where Marcette crooned to the baby.

"Where's Nafferton?" he shot at her.

"How do you know it was Nafferton?" she asked breathlessly.

"Eet was Nafferton!" Marcette quailed before the fire in his eyes. She nodded her head. "He went out last fall on the boat," she whispered.

So Jim had been mistaken! To please Nafferton Diana had used *Le Chat Civet!* No wonder he had caught its faint fragrance in Marcette's hair. It was in everything he picked up.

Père Vallois was silent. A load had been lifted from his mind. The events of this night explained Marcette's secretiveness.

Pierre turned to the window. He was ashamed to face Marcette. His mind was chaotic. The priest spoke:

"There are four of us now where there were only two this afternoon; but before this poor girl died we promised that her secret would be guarded. I want all of you to understand that her brother is not to know the truth."

They nodded. Marcette came to Pierre, the baby in her arms. The little mite caught the horny finger of the giant Frenchman in its tiny hand. It pulled Pierre back from the misty realms where his tortured mind wandered. Jim! The urgency of Jim's need came then at lightening speed.

He electrified Marcette with the announcement that Jim was at the Post at that very moment, a raving

115

madman. He told the priest how the Factor and he had searched the past hour for him.

"I keel a dog team bringin' heem from de creek in five day, an' den I stan' here helpless."

The rapidity with which things were happening was almost too much for Marcette. Her voice broke as she tried to ask Pierre how long Jim had been at the Post.

The little priest was calmest of them all.

"We can do no further good here, my friends. It is best we hurry to save the living. To-morrow we can arrange for the burial. We must agree that it would be unwise to the point of foolishness to acquaint this sick man with the news of to-night. Time will heal these wounds. Let us not ask, or question, the Divine Power which seeks these strange ways to accomplish Its ends."

Militantly he led the procession across the snow to the Post. Exhaustion had set in with Jim. Wide-eyed, he stared up at them. The little Father had sent for his medicine chest. Père Vallois ordered Marcette to her room where she and Aleekna sought to lull the child to sleep. Aleekna succeeded where the girl failed.

Pierre went sound asleep standing on his feet. The Factor caught him as he was about to topple over.

One by one they left the sick room — all but the man of God. Forty years of such days and nights he had put behind him. Nothing but the finely drawn steel of the man remained. Or maybe it was, as he said, that a heavenly hand reached down to help him on, to save him for his beloved North until another should come to carry on the Cross.

116

Morning found him still strong. Jim was no worse. That he would have the vitality to recover from the exposure of the long trip was the priest's bravest hope.

The news of the English girl's death soon spread.

The Post moved in quietness. Marcette tip-toed her way to Jim's beside. She sat beside him while Father Malotte hastened away to say his mass. In his delirium, Jim moaned and talked of things and places strange and unfamiliar to Marcette's ears. Mechanically, she did the little things the old Jesuit had told her to do.

Her father called her when the priest came back. The simple preparations for the burial were complete. From the little cabin to the graveyard on the sheltered hillside they bore the dead girl.

Death was something all of them could appreciate. Silently the men and women walked in their black clothes. Many of them had never exchanged a word with her whom they mourned. But life was simple there. Death wiped away at a stroke all thought of caste or prejudice.

Big Pierre knelt beside Marcette at the grave. Diana had opened a new world for her. To Marcette's credit be it said that she did not let Diana's misstep weigh against the dead girl. Diana had given everything for love. Her great mistake had been her choice of man.

Marcette wondered who was to take Diana's place in her life. The intimacy between them had grown and grown until it seemed she could not go on without her. Who would listen to her dreams of the future? To her ambitions? Other folks would laugh at her, were she to tell them. Diana had never laughed. She had seen in

117

Marcette a little imprisoned bird longing to fly, trying with its might to soar into space and life.

Tenderly Pierre led Marcette away. He remembered that the good Father had once said that no matter what the need, someone, or something would always arise to meet the occasion. He repeated the thought to her now.

"Eet's true, *ma chérie*. Dis tam' eet's Jim. You an' me got to save heem."

It was true. Yes, they had to save M'sieu' Jim.

Her chin quivered as she tried to speak.

"But the good God couldn't take him away, too, Pierre," she sobbed. "He couldn't do that to little Marcette."

Something in big Pierre Baptiste snapped at that. The tears rolled down his seamed cheeks. He had not forgotten his talk with Jim that night in the dug-out on the Windigo. Marcette was destined to lose him in the end, anyway.

An hour must have passed when the Factor called them.

The perspiration had broken on Jim. It was the first hopeful sign. Coming at this moment, it was a kindness from the hand of God. There was work for Marcette to do now. Gladly she turned to it. Life still held a promise.

CHAPTER
SIXTEEN

By Due Process
of Law

Nafferton, once he had arrived at Trois Riviers, did not go direct to his objective. His money was running low and his need of funds pressing. But he was gambler enough to wait until the Choate boys and Ritchie and the others had talked enough to bull the market.

But if Nafferton waited, so did the man he would ultimately have to see. Spider and fly waited and watched and only the spider suspected the other.

Trois Riviers had the dignity of a justice court once every three months. It was all the law it had needed to date. The business of lawing had not flowered in that part of the North. Still, one luckless practitioner had drifted in, in the years past, and although he flourished not and practiced never, he clung on. He had been ugly and heavy of jowl in his younger days, but then there had been a certain newness to him, which had compelled some deference.

Whence he came, no one asked. As men do, in river towns, he drifted in, built a cabin on the waterfront opposite Peter La Roche's saloon and dance hall, hung his sign to the wind and settled down to wait for customers. A. Z. Lester was his name.

There in his cupboard he waited. Trois Riviers smiled when some wag tacked an L onto his name. Henceforth he was Lazy Lester to all. It was too good a jest to be lost.

His Prince Albert went from shininess, through successive stages of grey, to bottle green as its owner grew fat and fingered the massive chain which anchored his watch to his bulging vest. And though he toiled not, he prospered. Men had waited to see him surround himself with the impedimenta of his profession, but they were doomed to be disappointed. His was a law office without books.

And yet men came to have a respect for this unlovely barrister. They found he carried enough law in his head to run the Dominion. He fought his battles outside the courtroom. Nobody fooled Lazy. Not even he, himself. He could put, or find, a joker in a contract that its own maker would not know was there.

And this was the man that Nafferton would eventually have to see. Lazy was the Journal, the news service extraordinary, of the river. But the news he gathered was for his consumption alone. No scandal or bit of gossip was too trivial to go unrecorded in his methodical mind.

He knew Nafferton was in town. He shrewdly divined the reason. Lazy had previous knowledge of the man. The Mannheims were beginning to pick up property in the Copper Kettle district. Lazy was not even up to the rank of a first class office boy with that big syndicate. But they did not hesitate to use him. He was their agent.

It amused him to note the assiduousness with which Nafferton avoided him. Another week would bring him to time. Lazy knew to a dollar the state of Nafferton's finances. The following week did bring him to Lazy's bailiwick.

Nafferton underestimated his opponent or else he would not have tried to spread such an air of prosperity. Old Lazy manicured his fingers with his paper cutter as the Englishman rattled on about the Windigo and the Misstassini. He should have taken warning from the progress of the manicuring going on before him.

Anxious prospectors, high-graders, free-traders, — all the varied assortment of hopeful ones who came to him, could have told Nafferton to go slow. The little finger they knew indicated an innocent to be trimmed. The middle finger, a man to be watched. The thumb, a crook.

Lazy was busy with the thumb.

He grew weary of Nafferton's harangue.

"Tell me what you have got to sell, Nafferton," he groaned. He stressed the accent on the "you."

"These!"

With a flourish Nafferton pulled out the location notices and affidavits stolen from Jim on the boat. The conversation was not the success he had expected.

"I hear you have bought out Ritchie and the Choates." He cast an inquiring eye at the man opposite him. "The Copper Kettle must look pretty good to the Mannheims. The grab begins already, eh?"

121

Lazy appeared not to have heard. He still operated on the recalcitrant thumb. His head buried on his chest, his heavy jowls spread fan-wise over his collar, he seemed for all the world like a neckless wonder. But his keen, piggy eyes followed Nafferton's every move.

"But what have you to sell?" he repeated, insidiously, this time he accented the "sell."

Nafferton walked to the window. This was the show-down. He tossed his handful of papers to the man at the table.

The lawyer toyed at them with the paper cutter. As he read he began on the other thumb. That meant not only a crook but a cut-throat to be watched.

All at once the cloak of indifference dropped away from Lester. The spider struck.

"You stole those notices and affidavits and you want us to hold the bag. Is that it?"

There was the rough cynicism of the man who knows the price of everything, the value of nothing, back of his question.

Nafferton stammered and hemmed and hawed, and Lester, lazy and indifferent again, poked at the thumb and waited. Nafferton settled down to the business he had come to Trois Riviers to put through.

"It's your property, or the property of the Mannheims, just as soon as you want the transfer made. I filed, through another man, location notices and affidavits of labor done last year on these claims. Here are copies of everything. The lines follow the original lines of the Stannard claims. Look them over and you'll see."

"Old stuff," Lazy said languidly.

"Very old," Nafferton answered. "But here's something else. For two years the Stannards paid McGarvy for doing the necessary annual assessment work demanded by law. Well, every day of those two years McGarvy was up on the Yukon. I've got proof of that. He wasn't here to do the work. That threw the ground open."

"McGarvy's dead, isn't he?" Lazy queried, again shifting the paper cutter, but still operating on the thumb.

"Been dead for six months or so. That makes it a cinch. The failure to do the work threw the ground back to the government. It has been relocated by me, and I want Stannard driven off. Get him out of the country."

"Oh, a personal grudge, eh? A woman, perhaps?"

The remittance-man did not answer.

"Come through, now," the oily one demanded. "It's a woman."

A fleeting vision of Diana held Nafferton. What a spectacle he would be married under such circumstances. He shivered.

"We'll keep the woman out of this," he muttered. "Not because she's too proud or virtuous; but because I prefer it that way. We'll talk shop."

Lazy smiled. It was better stuff than he had believed Nafferton possessed.

"There's gold on that creek," he went on. "It belongs to me now. If you want to share the risks, the profits will be big. You can drive Stannard away, or you can let him stay. I don't give a damn."

"You say this Stannard's working up there?"

"Yes! Stayed there all winter. Well, it will do him no good, I tell you. The ground has been relocated because it was open. Open, do you hear? I got hold of it legitimately."

Nafferton's voice rose until it jarred on Lazy. He stopped gouging his thumb. The deal was shady enough to warrant serious attention. He proceeded to draw up an agreement. It was worded in the usual way of legal documents and Nafferton studied it with the care of a layman who prides himself on knowing all the tricks.

He tossed it back to Lester.

"This gives you an option to buy," he grinned. "I'm not selling. Good day." He made a poor bluff at leaving.

Lazy's paper cutter came down with a bang.

"We'll do business no other way!" he shot at Nafferton.

They were fencing. An offer to sell outright was evidence enough that the seller had no faith in his property. It worked the other way, too. Gold claims of promise are not handled about in that manner.

"I want to be carried along for a half," Nafferton asserted. "Your people to pay all the expenses of getting the property into our possession. They can conduct the legal business, and work the mine. That's final."

The very abruptness of the demand, as much as its size, swung Lazy completely around to a firm belief in the merit of the claims.

124

He knew the district in the same way that he knew every mining district in the North. Strikes had been frequent of late. Perhaps Nafferton knew more than he told. Anyhow he was anxious. Anxiety has its origin in something.

"It will take some time to get my people moving," the great hulk asserted. But he made out a new agreement as he talked. And it gave Nafferton only one-third. Lazy was not giving everything away. They did business this time.

Nafferton agreed to find a man to guide their party to the claims when spring came. Both of them saw the expediency of sending a deputy marshal along with the engineer who would go in to report on the property.

The syndicate could be depended upon to look after those little details. They would have enough men there to hold it, once the mine was in their possession.

Nafferton walked on air as he left the lawyer's abode. He had an abiding faith in the property. He wanted it to win. Every other deal he had been in on had slipped up, somehow. Now he was backed by the most ruthless group of financiers in the mining game. They would stand back of their agreement, and take their two-thirds. It gave them the control they wanted. Nafferton was satisfied.

Wherever there was trouble between partners, disputes over ownership, or plain outright claim jumping, the Mannheim interests were sure to bob up. Like stormy petrels they heralded cloudy titles.

And they always operated within the law. With unlimited money they could afford to.

125

The Englishman knew that at Roubideaux he could find some Pointe Aux Barques runner who had been to the camp on the Windigo who would be willing to guide his party in. Nafferton had no intention of being there in person. Nor did he view with pleasure the trip to Roubideaux. He knew he was risking his neck.

He dreaded the thought of meeting Diana and the entanglements to be faced because of her. He even considered marriage as a way out. The North would not hold him long once he had received his advance.

Night after night in La Roche's bar-room, he brooded over the dangers of the trip which confronted him. There it was that the news of Diana's death reached him. It brought nothing but a wonderful sense of relief to Nafferton. Thank God, there was no talk of a baby. She had died suddenly. That, and the fact that Stannard was lying at the Post at the point of death, were the only facts he could worm out of the N. W. messenger.

If Stannard died he would be safe. He asked himself who could know of his relations with Diana. He shuddered at the thought of Pierre. If the girl had talked before she died, Pierre and Marcette would have been the ones to have heard her story. Then again, she might have kept still for her own sake.

He realized that old man Vallois could deny him the right to enter the Post if he were so minded. It wouldn't come to that, though. If he was suspected other means would be brought to bear to make him pay.

Pierre, for instance. Why was it that the hands of the giant Frenchman seemed everlastingly at his throat?

126

He made up his mind then and there that he would not return alone. Someone handy with a gun or knife would accompany him. Someone like MacTavish, or Muldoon. Trois Riviers was full of men like that. In some way he would get the money out of Lazy to finance this little affair.

When he arranged for his space with Captain MacNab, he got a parting shot from that individual not at all to his fancy.

"Your nae findin' the pickin's so gude doon this way?" the Scotchman questioned.

Nafferton glowered angrily at the old skipper. Then his good sense intervened and he laughed. He could afford to laugh now. His laugh would be the last one, too, and, therefore, best.

Did he not have the backing of the great Mannheim interests? This old fool with his flat-bottomed tub would still be sweating his soul away long after he had begun counting his millions.

It was too funny.

CHAPTER
SEVENTEEN

The Way of the North

Stannard lay in his bed at Roubideaux propped up by many pillows. He was thin to emaciation. The past weeks were a blank. All he could remember was the drift on the blind lead; the acrid smell of burning tallow and the cold and loneliness. He had no recollection at all of the manner in which Pierre had brought him to the Post.

It did not take Father Malotte's words to convince Jim that he owed his life to Marcette's tender and unremitting care. She, too, had aged under the strain of the sleepless days and nights. The incessant worry over the time when he should be told of Diana's death had weighed on her. Jim had borne the sad news stoically, as is the way with Anglo-Saxons.

Weakened by his long illness, he was pessimistic enough to torture himself for days with the thought that he had been responsible for bringing her into this lonely land. Had she been home this tragedy might never have occurred. And yet, it was to save her from herself that he had brought her here.

Father Malotte had told him it was typhoid — a kindly lie. True enough typhoid claimed its victims back home as well. The outcome of all this was to set him back for weeks.

Pierre had sold his furs and the sight of the long string of company counters he thought would cheer the sick man. It meant they should not want for months to come. Pierre's optimism did have some good effect on Jim. It, at least, got him into the way of thinking about the future.

Jim smiled at Pierre wanly.

"You are still willing to waste your time on the Windigo?" he asked.

"Oh, but yes. By April you be all right. We'll try once more. Eef we don' fine not'ing by fall we'll quit for sure."

"Well, it did look better the last day or two we were there. Both of us know there is a pot of gold on that creek waiting for the lucky man to turn it up. I've been doing a lot of thinking, lying here day after day. I've found out one thing."

"Bout de mine?" Pierre questioned.

"No, not about the mine. About gold! I've found out that all the gold is not in the ground. Some of it is right here in this room." He paused. "I wonder why Marcette and you have been so kind to me? You have stopped at nothing in my behalf."

"*Mon jee*, you mak' me mad, Jim, talk lak' dat. Dat Marcette, she's kin' lak' dis to ever'body. You know dat. She's nevaire hurt not'ing." Pierre started for the door. "Tam' for you to tak' a nap now. I come back by'm-bye. But don' mak' no talk lak' dat again."

129

Jim heard him tramping down the stairs. His eyes were misty. It was the way of the North. Give you all; do everything for you; but don't ever try to thank them.

He dozed off for an hour. Visions of Cecilie and Marcette pursued each other as he slept. He had had plenty of time to think of Cecilie. He had heard from her again. It was a friendly letter. The kind he knew he should expect. Love seemed to be only a matter of secondary importance in her busy life of pleasure.

Jim had wondered if it would not be the honorable and wisest thing to write Cecilie and release her from her promise. It seemed a cowardly thing to do, at that. Ken would never consent to it.

Long before he opened his eyes, Jim knew that Marcette was in the room. He had felt her hand brush him. She must have bent over him to have seen whether or not he really slept. The sweet fragrance of her breath had come to him. It reminded him of the smell of grass in early spring. Her freshness was far more intoxicating to Jim than the rarest of perfumes could have been.

Undoubtedly from Pierre, he had formed the habit of regarding her as a child. That elusion was gone now. Marcette had grown in the year he had known her. The well-rounded bosom, the curve of her dainty ankles, all told him she had become a woman.

He envied Pierre the day that he should win her. But a grave doubt of that ever coming to pass had entered his mind. His days of nearness to Marcette had given him a chance to see, as Diana had, that her thoughts wandered far from the North.

130

Stannard loved her frankness. She did not pretend to be what she was not. More than once he damned the sophistication that made him see her mistakes, her meagre education and her ridiculous faith in people in general.

Marcette stopped her crooning. She became aware of Jim's gaze. She smiled at him and came to the bedside. He caught her hand.

"Why stop?" he begged. "You know I love it."

He held her eyes with his own until her face colored.

"Why did Pierre leave so soon?" she asked.

"Oh, I tried to tell him how grateful I am for all he has done. He is as bad as you are. He refused to listen and tried as usual to make light of it."

That made Marcette smile.

"You know, M'sieu' Jim, that we do not like to be reminded about the little things we do for you."

"Couldn't you drop the m'sieu' thing, Marcette, for once? Couldn't you call me just — Jim?"

The look in Stannard's eyes embarrassed her. But she smiled and nodded her head as she murmured "Yes — Jim."

Stannard was happy for the first time in months as he watched her flitting about the room, preparing his supper. For the hundredth time he caught himself comparing her with the girl he had promised to marry.

He saw gracefulness in every movement as she busied herself for him. The well-rounded arms, the finely chiseled head, all appealed to Stannard. He tried in vain to banish the wild thoughts that her nearness sent scurrying through his mind.

131

She placed his tray on the bed and fed him. They were like children. Once Jim laughed so heartily he frightened her.

André and Pierre came in then. The Factor had just received word that the boat would arrive in the morning. There was unsuppressed excitement at the Post that night.

It made Stannard turn back the clock. Just a year ago he and his sister had come to Roubideaux. What a year of working and suffering it had been! He fretted himself into a fever, worrying about the past, before sleep came with its thankful oblivion.

From his window the next morning, he witnessed a repetition of the scene he had been a part of last spring. He wondered if there would be mail, or news for him. He understood, now, what that first boat meant.

The exertion was too much for him. Before all of the passengers had come ashore he dropped back to the safety of his bed. Therefore he did not see the silent drama enacted on the landing.

Nafferton had not gone back on his promise to Lazy. He was here on schedule, moving in the ominous shadow of Mr. Muldoon. They were among the last to leave the boat. Mr. Muldoon's hands were not encumbered by any troublesome hand-baggage.

The priest, the Factor, Marcette and Pierre exchanged a shrewd glance at the sight of him. The others might have felt that the man's presence augured some last minute's resolve to right the wrong he had committed. Not so Pierre. He knew Muldoon quite well. And he knew that Nafferton was a coward.

Cowards do not take chances like this unless they are stark, raving mad. Something of great import alone could have forced Nafferton to thrust his head into the lion's mouth.

Pierre lounged across the platform until he stood directly in his path. Nafferton was fishy white about the face. The gauntlet was thrown down if he and his hired warrior cared to take it up.

Like a towering menace, Pierre stood before them and Nafferton and Muldoon turned aside. When they met the issue it would not be in broad daylight, before a hostile crowd. The dark served their purpose best.

Pierre turned to catch Nafferton's backward glance. It was for all the world like the look of a rat that had slipped through the paws of a cat and felt a sense of safety in flight.

Muldoon and his master inspired no fear in the big Frenchman. But a consuming curiosity arose within him as to what brought them here.

The Englishman did not go to his old cabin. The memories there were not ones to bring any peace of mind to him. Instead he found lodgings at La Pointe's place.

After the mail had been sorted and read, Father Malotte, the Factor and Pierre, met for consultation as if by appointment.

Père Vallois was the first to speak.

"The thing for me to do is to send him away at once. The impertinence of the man in venturing back here is unbelievable."

"Who knows, maybe, there is some latent good in the man," the little priest interrupted him to say. "At least he can give the child a name."

Marcette entered in time to hear the Jesuit's words.

"No, no!" she said excitedly. "He will not take the child away from here. What chance would he have with a man like that for a father? As for a name, what better name could he have than the one we gave him?"

Marcette referred to the christening at which she and Pierre had stood sponsors for Diana's baby.

"Don't you worry, *ma petite*," Pierre assured her. "I don' give dat little feller ma good name for not'ing. Nobody goin' tak' heem. Eef Père Vallois send dis man away, Jim ees goin' t'ink sumt'ing pretty funny. Leave heem to me. I fin' out what brings heem back here."

Luck played into Nafferton's hands an hour after his arrival. In the bar-room he found Joe La Flamme, who had been with La Voie, the time Jim was brought to the Post from the Windigo.

He could have returned that night to Trois Riviers had the boat been ready to sail. But it would be a week at least before her cargo was made up. All he had to do now was to lie low and race down river at the first opportunity. Nothing could spoil his plans this time.

Nafferton had agreed to take La Flamme with him. He was not taking the chance of leaving him behind to talk.

In the meantime, he stuck to his room and Pierre was at a loss to discover the business that had brought him back.

134

CHAPTER
EIGHTEEN

The Fangs of the Wolf

Had it not been for a chance bit of gossip, that drifted to Nafferton one evening as he ate his supper, it is probable that he would have sailed away at the end of the week without a word having been said.

Marcette was everlastingly admonishing Pierre not to draw a fight with him. She did not want Jim to suspect that Nafferton had returned. She knew Jim would insist on seeing him. So well had they kept their secret that Stannard bore no ill-will toward the man who had injured him so repeatedly. Nafferton was undoubtedly a fool, and out of place in the North. But to Jim he was still an Englishman.

The girl and the others took it for granted that Nafferton was aware of the child. It was on this that they based all of their thoughts and suspicions regarding him.

Hence they would not have understood why he perked up his ears at the bare mention of a baby in the Vallois household.

Two men were talking. One was trying to convince the other that no Indian woman had ever given birth to a blond baby.

Nafferton leaned closer. Perspiration began to moisten his forehead.

"Why you'll see blondes and brunettes in the same family, if you travel much among the Nascaupees and Montagnais," his partner asserted. "There's lots of left-handed goings on, in this country."

"Maybe so, sometimes, but not in this case. Vallois' old squaw was never the mother of that kid."

Nafferton went directly to his room. "What did it mean?" he asked himself, when he had bolted the door. "God — I might have known!" he groaned. He peered through the window at the Post. He would have given anything to have been able to steal in there and see this child with his own eyes.

Every time Muldoon moved, in the next room, it sent a shiver down his spine. Three days more and then he could make a dash for it! In some way he would see old Aleekna before then.

His best chance came the very next morning. Pierre was busy superintending the loading of the N. W. bales. Aleekna would be sure to be sunning herself in the shelter of the new wing of the Post. The Factor would be at the landing. Quickly then he called Muldoon, and off they went.

Jim had received the draft which had been so long delayed. It was for a tidy sum. It buoyed him up. He could stand on his own legs again as long as it lasted. Marcette watched him as he hobbled his first few steps about the room.

The sun was shining. It was glorious out, with a nip still in the air. He saw from his window the busy men

THE FANGS OF THE WOLF

toiling at the fur house and on the deck of the boat. Thus it was that his eyes wandering aimlessly about discovered Nafferton talking to the squaw whom he had found as he had expected.

Jim called to Marcette. In an instant she saw that all of their subterfuge and concealment had come to naught. He pointed to the Englishman.

"There is Nafferton! See! Talking to Aleekna. I thought you told me he was down river?"

Marcette tried to conceal her embarrassment.

"He came in on the boat, Monday."

"Does he know that I have been laid up here for weeks?"

There was a double question in Stannard's words. Marcette felt it.

"Everyone knows you have been very sick," she answered.

"Seems strange Nafferton has not dropped in to see me." He paused then until he caught her eyes. "Maybe you object to his coming here?"

"No, no," Marcette hurried to reply. She did not know what else to say.

"Well then, if you don't, would you mind asking him to come up for a minute? I would like to talk to him."

For a second Jim's request made her panicky. But she was not one to turn away from difficulties that had to be met. She would have a minute with Nafferton before he saw Jim. She made a move to start when he called her back.

Jim had seen Nafferton grow vehement as he harangued the old squaw. Aleekna turned away. The baby, which she carried, reached up his hands to catch at Nafferton's coat.

"Look at that," Jim smiled, "the man has one friend, anyway."

Even as he spoke he saw Nafferton snatch his coat away angrily. Marcette bit her lips.

"That's rank ingratitude, what?" Jim protested. Aleekna started to cross to the door. The sun caught the little blond head in its rays then.

"Whose youngster is that?" Jim asked the girl beside him.

Marcette stammered. She tried to conceal her confusion.

"A — Aleekna's, I suppose. One of her Nascaupee grandchildren."

"That's strange, isn't it? A blond Indian. I wonder why she does not carry it on her back?" Fortunately, for Marcette, Nafferton began to walk away. She ran down the stairs to catch him.

The man at the window saw dumb surprise on Nafferton's face as Marcette stopped him. He noted also that Muldoon cleared for action. Nafferton must have made some protest against coming up at that moment. He did not know what it was Marcette said then; but it swung the man around in a hurry. They came back.

Once out of sight of Jim's inquisitive eyes Marcette turned on Nafferton like a white fury.

"Don't mistake the circumstances under which you enter. M'sieu' Stannard saw you and asked for you. Don't stay long. If Pierre should find you here your life would not be worth that." She snapped her fingers. "Your friend does not suspect you in any way. He believes his sister died of the fever. Never, by any word or thought, have we hinted of a child. Until five minutes ago he had never seen the baby."

It was too good to be true! Nafferton began to live again. He started up the stairs. Marcette held him back.

"Wait," she murmured, the hatred of the man creeping into her voice, "you don't have to turn so white. You have nothing to fear from him. I know you would stoop to anything, but don't you let him know 'bout Diana. The other man will wait here with me. For ten minutes you go. If you're not back then, I'll call Pierre Baptiste."

Marcette heard Jim open the door above, as Nafferton ascended the stairs. She had only finished in time.

Muldoon eyed her with pleasure. He could understand a woman who could lay down the law that way. He made an attempt to start a conversation, but gave up in disgust. Then he settled himself in the sunshine to wait for the man he followed.

Marcette lived a year in every one of the minutes Nafferton was with Jim. What was he telling Stannard? If she had known, she might well have worried.

Nafferton saw in Jim a shadow of the man he had known. It was like him, once free of impending disaster, to rush into another. He hated Stannard. Chiefly because he was clean and straight-going. He was trickster enough himself to realize that the deception they were practicing on Jim would not hold up forever.

139

As long as he was not suspected he racked his brain to find some scheme by which he could, once for all, throw his guilt on another's shoulders.

He had a dozen excuses for not having been around earlier. He went to some length to explain the mythical business which had brought him to Roubideaux.

It concerned the establishing of a freight route to the Choate claims on the Misstassini. Did Jim know that they had sold out to the Mannheims? It immediately turned their talk to the sacred channel of mining. When Nafferton looked at his watch he found that his time was up. He reiterated his sorrow at Diana's death.

From the half-opened door he could look down to where Marcette waited for him. He nodded knowingly to Stannard.

"The Factor's little daughter seems terribly interested in you. I guess you have not wanted for anything."

"She has been very kind to me. I owe my life to her."

"Sounds like you were interested in her, too, eh?"

"What do you mean?" Jim had caught the sneer back of Nafferton's words.

"That it looks like a pleasant little adventure to me. I congratulate you, Jim. You've excellent taste."

The studied insult in his words drove Jim furious.

"Close that door," he said angrily, "before she hears any more of your talk."

"Well, it wouldn't hurt her if she did. She's got the hide of a burro."

Jim's rising temper proved to him how weak he really was. He actually trembled as he faced Nafferton.

"Stop," he cried. "I'm in no condition to make you take that back. But I resent it. I'll —"

"You resent it?" Nafferton cut in. "You, engaged to a girl back home, resent it because I unconsciously hit the nail on the head?" He laughed. "It was a chance shot." He went on. "I little dreamed you were in love with that savage."

Jim gasped. Was it true, then? Had he laid Marcette open to this insult because of his engagement to Cecilie?

Nafferton opened the door again.

"Don't take it so hard," he admonished. "When you were at the window a little while back perhaps you noticed old Aleekna with that squalling kid in her arms. Ask Marcette about that baby sometime when you've got a little leisure. Its name is Pierre."

Jim's eyes blurred with dizziness as he cried out for Nafferton to stop. He raised his hands to strike, but Nafferton was gone.

The world reeled around Stannard's head. Was everything wrong and bad? Was the world as rotten as this?

Marcette could get nothing out of him. He was strangely cool and aloof. The old intimacy seemed to have been destroyed by the advent of Nafferton. Nothing could come of telling Pierre of the Englishman's visit.

Disinterestedly Jim watched the departure of the boat. Nafferton and Muldoon sailed away. La Flamme went along also, but his going was unnoticed.

For days Jim conserved his strength. He could not rest until he had talked with the old Indian servant. Nafferton had told the truth. Aleekna called the child, Pierre.

The change it wrought in Jim was too noticeable to escape attention. There was no one he could turn to to confirm or contradict the suspicions that were eating him up.

Pierre began preparations for the trip to the Windigo. But even this did not bring back a smile to the Englishman's lips. Marcette knew in some way Nafferton was to blame; but she, even as Jim, dared not force a question on the subject.

April days sent the hills green and turned the woods into a riot of color. He was strong enough to get about now. Pierre waited for him. He wondered if Jim had discovered the lie with which they had shielded him. What else could have worked such a change in him?

Stannard saw the hurt look in the eyes of his two friends. He knew they were as miserable as himself. It seemed a poor reward for all they had done for him.

He tried to believe that Nafferton had lied. The man was worse than a coward. And yet he remembered Marcette's hesitation the time he had asked her about the child; both her and Pierre's poorly concealed objection to having Nafferton visit him; the undeniable fact that the baby bore the big fellow's name.

It could not be that the Factor was fooled, too. It was all so mysterious, but behind the seemingly contradictory facts lurked something that was being withheld.

142

Many times during the long canoe trip to the mine Pierre sought to draw him out and, with even more shrewdness, Jim did likewise. It was a subject that set up danger signals at even the most distant approach. Like two cagey, trapwise wolves they walked 'round and 'round it and got nowhere.

The actual opening up of the old drift did bring them together for a time. In spite of himself Jim warmed to the thrill of being on the job.

His health and strength flew back in the open. Both men were quick to realize that the mine got more promising day after day. They left the jumbled porphyry quartz and syenite behind. The vein began to run between two clearly defined walls filled with highly mineralized quartz.

As they crept forward, further and further under the hill, the values increased. It had a peculiar effect on Jim. For better than a year he had slaved his very life away on this venture. The renewed promise of the reward tended to make him only more quiet and glum. He lived within himself. How much less it would mean now, if it came, than it would have six months ago!

Pierre knew they were nearing their goal. Either the vein would pinch out or they would send a drill into a jewelery shop one of these mornings. Jim's increased reticence, his quietness and his desire to be alone, awakened a queer suspicion in the Frenchman's mind.

Was it possible that Jim regretted the fact that under the law of the mining game, he would have to surrender half of the earnings to him? It was a grubstake deal now. The thought that Stannard could feel that way

143

after what they had been through, sickened him. What else could it be?

Saturday came and Pierre knocked off at noon. It was cold and damp in the drift. The woods beckoned him. He told Jim he was through for the day. Jim's answer was short, even curt. He didn't see how a man could quit, while strength and light lasted, at a time like this. He ate his lunch and returned to the shaft by himself.

The laughing woods and the brooks running full to their banks reminded Pierre, too plainly, of the pleasure and happiness he had always known. He had not laughed in weeks. He laughed now, but there was no mirth in it. Its hollowness shocked him.

Greed he could understand. He had seen men turn on life-long friends because of it. Stannard seemed beyond that. Bit by bit he had broken down Pierre's natural repugnance for the outsider. Once he had taken a liking to him, he would have stopped at nothing.

An idea to fly, to get away in a hurry, was born within him. Why stay on? The gold meant little to him. He laughed again. Well he knew it was all rightly his, if he cared to make it so.

He came back to the dug-out. A few minutes sufficed for him to gather his duffle. He threw his bag in one of the canoes and paddled away. No backward glance for him this time. As he swung into the river his heart grew lighter. He even tried a song.

Thus it was that he did not see the wild man who danced and yelled from the mouth of the shaft. It was Jim. He had the look of a maniac. An hour ago he had felt the drill go squashing into a pocket. Cleverly he had blown out the retaining wall. Before him lay exposed the gold chimney.

On his hands and knees he petted and caressed the precious metal. They were rich! Wealth beyond his wildest dreams lay before them! He laughed and cried alternately. He scrambled out of the drift and up the shaft. He called and called; but Pierre did not answer him.

He ran to the dug-out. He noticed that Pierre's things were gone. The Frenchman's canoe was missing, too.

At first the knowledge that Pierre had left threw him into a violent rage. All of these weeks he had kept back his suspicions of him. If he had been cool and aloof it was to spare Pierre. What had gotten into the man, to send him off this way?

He flung himself face down in the grass. He thought of Marcette. What sort of an explanation would he make to her? He fathomed his mind to discover some other reason that could have sent Pierre off.

"My God," he muttered, and sat bolt upright. "The mine!" he cried. "Could he have thought I didn't want him to have his share?"

He ran to the hill that overlooked the river. In the distance he could see a canoe. "Come back," he yelled. "Pierre! Pierre!"

But there was no answering call. Pierre Baptiste was a mile away, his canoe speeding down to Roubideaux.

CHAPTER
NINETEEN

To Get an Education

A strange sight met Pierre's eyes at Roubideaux. The boat was at the landing, its decks piled high with freight. A score of tents had been erected below the Post. The news of the Mannheim move had filtered south. With that wild frenzy a gold rush induces, men had hurried into the North with every conceivable kind of equipment.

Nafferton was back again. Knowing Pierre and Jim to be on the Windigo, he had not feared to return. By his presence he hoped to speed things along, inasmuch as the syndicate would not give up until they had a report on his property.

Grace, the Company's engineer, was with him; also Muldoon and a dozen others including Bellew, the marshal.

Pierre noticed the pile of mining equipment they had brought along. He saw Nafferton talking excitedly to one of the group. He had arrived the day previous, and with the sure knowledge that Jim and Pierre were away, and knowing the strength of the force in back of him, the Englishman had swelled out to a man of considerable importance.

146

Pierre sat in his canoe for ten minutes before he trudged up to the Post. Marcette faced him as he threw his bag on the floor. She was thoroughly surprised to see him.

"What has happened?" was her first question.

"Not'in' happen! I jus' get t'rough, dat's all. For t'ree week I stan' dat dam' fool! For t'ree week he mak' no talk wid me excep' to ask f'r sumt'in. Now he can have de whole mine eef he wants heem. I fine eet for heem, an' soon as she begin to look good, *Mon Dieu*, he act lak' he don' want me dere."

For half an hour Marcette plied him with questions before she could understand what had caused the break between the two men. Like Pierre, she wondered if it had been the mine that had worked the change in Jim which they had felt even before he had left for the creek.

The excitement at Roubideaux was easier explained. The Factor saw Pierre's prophecy coming true. This gold rush boded ill for the fur industry.

"See," he berated Pierre, "you start all this. Weren't you the first one to wag your tongue about this infernal gold? And now, what have you got out of it? This Englishman will laugh at you the rest of his life if he makes a strike."

"No, he won't laugh at me, Père Vallois," Pierre cried angrily. "I go now to Trois Riviers wid MacNab. Nobody goin' laugh at me."

"We'll see," the Factor replied, as he went on with his work. "The North is for our own kind. You have wasted a year and a half chasing his rainbows. I'll admit he

147

seemed different from the rest of his kind. I had really learned to be fond of the man. I suppose Marcette will find some excuse for him. Women are that way."

Pierre smoked his pipe in silence as André worked on his books. Nafferton's destination aroused the big man's curiosity.

"Where do you t'ink dis Nafferton ees headed for?" He cocked an eye at the older man. "Do you believe dat tale 'bout de Misstassini?"

André dropped his pen.

"All day long I've tried to find that out. If it were not for Bellew I would almost believe it. But they have no need of a marshal over there."

Pierre whirled on Père Vallois at that.

"*Mon jee,*" he cried. "Suppose dis Nafferton did steal dose papers from Jim? Maybe dey hear eet look pretty good now. *Voila,* he file dem, an' come on de run wid dis gang, eh?"

He laughed at the picture he had sketched.

"By Gar, I tak' a han' in dat. I bat Jim goin' have some fun." His fist clinched. "Dat's hall right he wan' me to go. I go; but I guess I giv' dat Nafferton a dam' fine laugh, too."

André watched him march off in search of MacNab.

While Pierre and the Factor had talked, Nafferton had marshaled his forces and got them under way. A clean saving of two days. With a sense of relief he and Muldoon watched the brigade paddle away. Nafferton knew he would be back in Trois Riviers by the time they reached the creek. Once there, he could hide out indefinitely if trouble should follow.

148

He sent Muldoon off to put their luggage aboard the *Morning Mist*. MacNab would get away sometime during the evening. Leisurely he followed his man in the general direction of La Pointe's. With a great deal of relish he feasted his eyes on the ragged buildings and chance people he passed. To a certainty he was taking his last look at them.

Marcette had been off on the hillside by herself trying to compose her upset mind. She was frightfully unhappy. No one had arisen to take Diana's place in her life. She knew her chances of realizing the ambitions the English girl had planted within her were slim indeed. This estrangement between Jim and Pierre would inevitably widen the gap between Jim and herself.

They had been very happy together until Nafferton had shown up. Win or lose, Jim would undoubtedly leave the North now. She wondered if he suspected how much he meant to her. Her heart sank when she compared herself with the grand ladies he must know down in Quebec or in far-away England. They would laugh at her and her rough clothes. Maybe Jim had sensed that. Maybe that was why he had seemed so cool of late.

From the elevation where she sat she saw the brigade depart, and gathering the flowers she had picked, she started home.

At the corner of the Fort she ran into Nafferton. She was a picture in her downcast mood, her arms filled with white blossoms. He smiled to himself as he watched her approach. He stepped in front of her. Only then did Marcette become aware of him.

He caught both of her arms with his hands. Marcette squirmed and tried to twist away from him. Nafferton laughed.

"You beautiful little devil," he purred. "Are you still angry with me?"

"Let me go," she cried as she fought him off.

"I'll let you go when I get good and ready. Why do you throw yourself away on Stannard? He hasn't a nickel to his name. Another month and he will be begging hand-outs. I could do something for you. I'll be a rich man in four weeks. I'd give you a chance to do something with that voice of yours. You're not fool enough to waste the rest of your life in this Godforsaken country, are you?"

Marcette struggled until she broke away and faced him, her eyes flashing fire.

"You shall pay for this," she panted. "You would run from a man."

"From Stannard, perhaps?" he asked sarcastically. "Try and win him if you can. Did he ever tell you he was engaged to a girl back home? I thought he hadn't told you that. He is interested in you all right. But not in the way you think."

Nafferton's temper ran away with him then. He threw aside any fancied chance he might have had with her.

"You didn't think for a minute, did you, that he would ever take you back to England? Why you are just a little backwoods, country kid. You haven't any

150

manners or education. People would laugh at you over there with your half b-r-r —"

The word "breed" was never finished. Like an avenging fury a body hurled itself at him from around the corner of the building. It was the giant Frenchman. He had stood on the landing watching the big flotilla paddle away. In one of the canoes he had recognized the red-shirted La Flamme. It satisfied him that they were headed for the Windigo.

MacNab was not aboard his boat, and coming back by way of the fur house, he had overheard Nafferton's blighting words.

He picked the remittance-man up as if he were a hissing kitten and slammed him down in the dust. The force of the fall left Nafferton winded and inert. Pierre picked him up and stood him on his wobbly legs. With one hand he held him erect and started his other from the knees to strike him. If the blow had ever been delivered Nafferton would have gone sprawling for twenty feet, his very ribs knocked in.

With all her weight Marcette caught at the moving arm as it gathered strength to strike.

"Pierre!" she cried. "Please don't hit him again. You'll kill him."

Pierre hesitated long enough to glance at her. She was in a fighting mood herself. Nafferton's words had sent a white heat scorching through her brain. All of her half-taken resolves were crystallized now.

"You bat I keel heem." Pierre glared at her. "For a year I wait for dat. Why you mak' me stop?"

Pierre sensed a feeling of steel striking steel as Marcette answered him.

"What he says is the truth. I am an ignorant, backwoods kid. I haven't any education or manners. But I am going to get them! I'm going to leave Roubideaux to-night with you. For three months I have been aching to go. That beast has done me a favor. He has made up my mind for me. Let him go."

Hopelessly, Pierre lowered his hands. Nafferton needed no second invitation to sneak away from the man he had supposed hundreds of miles to the North.

"But, Marcette, I don' laugh when you talk," Pierre expostulated. "Père Vallois he don' laugh."

Marcette squeezed his hand.

"I know you wouldn't, my good friend. But these others, who do not know me, would."

"Well, I go many place. Always I talk dis English. Nobody evaire laugh at me."

Marcette knew she could not explain what she meant without hurting his feelings. But by the time they reached the Factor she had Pierre on her side.

Marcette's request was a blow to old André, even though she was to go under Pierre's protection. He knew Trois Riviers for a wild town. He never would have consented to her going by herself.

"For two, tr'ee week, dat's all," Pierre counseled him. "She got seeck of dat plac' 'for long, an' den I bring her back. Dat crazy old Luigi, who play de piano for La Roche, he know dam' soon eef she got a voice. Eef you don' let dat chile go now, by Gar, she worry you all de res' your life."

152

André shook his head.

"Maybe so," he replied. "But I don't like this business. Roubideaux was good enough for her mother. She never was ashamed of the North."

Captain MacNab came in then and he had a word to say.

"You're daft, man," he said. "Times hae changed. Gie her a chance to try her wings. She'll be nae the worse for it."

"All right, she can go," the Factor agreed. "Pack your things, and you, MacNab, see that she has the best. *Mon Dieu*, what's this country coming to? Have we all gone mad chasing rainbows?"

Marcette did not wait to hear her father rail on. Long before sailing time she had packed her portmanteau and cautioned Aleekna about the child's care.

It was her first trip to Trois Riviers, and MacNab took a keen delight in showing her about the boat and in pointing out his pet spots along the river.

Two of his passengers were badly indisposed throughout the entire trip. They were Nafferton and Mr. Muldoon. Not once did they put in an appearance. But their recovery was complete and sudden once the *Morning Mist* had tied up in Trois Riviers.

Nafferton hurried off to find Lester, the Mannheim agent. He wanted him to know that one of the men who had been working the claims on the Windigo was in town. Lazy would have known in due time without his assistance. For, an hour after Pierre had left the recorder's office, word was brought to Lazy of his

153

presence and of the puzzling fact that he had filed six claims on the Mistageux.

Lazy got rid of Nafferton in a hurry. He sat out the morning trying to figure why a man from the Windigo would be filing property on a creek miles away. He gave it up in disgust. Lazy was too wise, though, to put it down as a Frenchman's whim. He knew Pierre Baptiste to be not that kind of a fool.

CHAPTER
TWENTY

In the Name of
the Law

Two weeks to the day from the time Jim had made his rich strike Bellew and his crowd set foot on the Windigo.

The two or three days following Pierre's departure had been idle ones. Stannard's sense of fair play would never for an instant have let him harbor a thought of withholding or regretting the dividing of the fortune he had found.

He had been alone before on the Windigo and no such feeling of isolation, as held him now, had rested on him. A man's morals might be a disappointment to another; but they were a man's own affair. It was quite another matter to have a tale go out that a partner had gone back on the one who had grubstaked him. He understood full well how such a story would brand a man in the North.

He resolved to get out the exposed pocket and stringers and go back to the Post himself. He found it slow work alone. A week elapsed before he had completed his task. What he had taken out was a pure quill and represented a tidy fortune.

Day after day he had cached the ore in a covert by the creek. It was not as a safeguard, but only as a time-saver against the day when he should leave, that he did this. In all the months he had been on the creek he had never seen a man, except at times when Pierre had gone out of his way to signal a Pointe Aux Barques runner or train. A thought of claim-jumpers or high-graders had never entered his mind.

So it is easy to realize his surprise when along toward supper-time he heard someone call: "Hello the house!" He dropped the fry-pan and went to the open door.

Grace, the engineer, was nominally in charge of the party; but Bellew, the marshal, was the real leader. He had served the Mannheims many years and owed his position to them. He had spread his men and surrounded the dug-out before he called.

Jim saw Bellew as he stood by the canoe landing. Almost at the same time he caught the glint of a rifle barrel moving in the bush to the man's right. In the clearing far to the left another man crouched.

It did not take Stannard long to realize that he was in for a run with trouble of some sort. He barred the door and seized his rifle. Through the window, in the dying light, he could see men moving. He tried to count them. There were at least a dozen.

Bellew called again, and the man in the dug-out cried back for him to come to the door alone. He saw the marshal unbuckle his gun and drop it on the ground before he moved up from the creek bottom. It

156

was dark in the dug-out now, and Jim had no trouble in watching him as he advanced.

Bellew pounded on the door with his fist.

"Open in the name of the law!" he thundered.

The law? Stannard had heard of that ruse being used by claim-jumpers since claims first were jumped.

"What's your game?" he shouted through the open window.

"Open in the name of the law!" Bellew repeated. "I've got a warrant for your arrest."

"I'll take a look at any warrant you've got for me. Drop it through the window. If that gun you dropped back there was a stage trick, you go slow with the other one. Just drop it through the window — I'll get it. And if you make a gun-play, I'll drop you cold."

Bellew hastened to oblige him. He preferred to do things in a legal way any time he could. Some of these tenderfoots could throw a gun pretty well.

Jim retreated to the little cubby-hole where he kept his supplies. He lighted a candle and read the warrant. It was legal as far as he could discover. The seals were in order. It called for the arrest of himself for working and holding in his possession a mine, or mines, alleged to be the property of the Mannheim Mining and Milling Company, a corporation.

"Come on, you damned claim-jumper or we'll blow your head off," somebody yelled. He was immediately rebuked by Bellew.

"Hold up there," he cried. "We're going to do this thing in a thoroughly legal way."

157

Bellew's manner had a reassuring effect on Jim. Apparently there was some law even in this wilderness.

"There must be some mistake, Marshal," he called to Bellew. "This is my property. My father bought these claims five years ago. I didn't come all the way from England on nothing."

"You'll have to tell that to the court. The best thing you can do is to open up. You're resisting arrest right now."

There did not seem to be any other way out of it. He had no chance of beating off ten or a dozen men. Sullenly he opened the door.

His conversation with the deputy had given the others the opportunity to surround the dug-out. A minute after he had unbolted the door he was lying on the floor bound hand and foot.

Even though the decision had been rendered quickly, Jim saw that he had pretty well banged up two of Bellew's crew. The marshal regarded him with amusement.

"The boys are inclined to be a little rough, I'm afraid. You mustn't hold it against them. They're just playful."

This man-handling went rather against the grain with Grace.

"Have you got anything to back up your statements that this property belongs to you?" he asked. "Any assessment receipts, or location notices?"

"They were stolen from me the day I arrived at Roubideaux, a year and a half ago. I've got last year's papers."

"They won't help you any. You had a chance to refile if the property was open — you should have done it, if it ever belonged to you. I hear you've got a good thing."

"You'll have to find that out for yourself. You can hardly expect me to help you to loot my own mine."

"It may have been your mine once, my boy, but here are the papers for it," Bellew cut in.

"You verified all these, Marshal?" Jim asked.

"I ain't getting no warrant from a judge unless they're all right. That ain't the way we do business up here, nohow. You'll go back to trial in Trois Riviers."

"Trial?" Jim shouted.

"Sure! You been looting a mine that belongs to these men. Where have you hid the stuff?"

"I hope I tell you that. Why, I worked and worked —"

"Yeh! Suppose you worked a bank the same way?" he asked. "— while the owners were out to lunch or getting a drink?"

"Well, the law will protect me," Jim answered, forgetting the indignities it had so lately heaped on his head.

"That's not my business," Bellew said as he stretched himself. "I do my duty as I see it. We'll make an early start down river in the morning. But there's no use keeping you trussed up all night. Untie him, Mose. Give him something to eat, too. You can sit up if you want to," he went on, addressing Stannard again.

Visions of himself in court as a high-grader and claim-jumper brought the perspiration to Jim's brow. Thank God, people back home would not be likely to

159

know. Bad enough that Marcette and Pierre and the others here in the North should have to witness his degradation.

The men smoked after supper and soon made themselves comfortable for the night. The long pull up the river had tired them out thoroughly. Jim studied their faces. La Flamme's brought no recollection. But he was sure he would know them all if he ever met them again.

The heavy breathing and snoring of the men about him kept him wide-awake. In the darkness he tried to free his bound hands. He rubbed the rope against the log of the bunk. It loosened a little.

For the first time thought of escape came to him. No one guarded the canoes. He could get to Roubideaux before any of them or lose himself in the wilderness below the Post. The ore he had cached would be safe where it was. He had a good share of the cash he had received from England in the wallet beneath him.

He slipped one hand through the noose that bound his arms together. A second pull and one hand was free. His captors' heavy breathing told him where they lay. He avoided them and gathered the things needed for his flight.

A beef-tin rattled to the floor. Jim sank under the table and waited. One of the men turned over and cursed. In a few minutes their deep, regular breathing told him it was safe to go on.

The chief barrier was the door. Inch by inch he opened it, its squeaking seeming to raise a din that could be heard for a mile. When he had closed it, and no one had moved, he heaved a sigh of relief.

He ran to his canoe and his running shove sent it well across the creek.

Ten minutes after he was gone one of the men on the dug-out floor sat up and laughed. Bellew lit the lamp.

"He's gone," he smiled. "I thought I'd die when he knocked that beef-tin off the table."

Even Grace could appreciate the situation.

"I'll bet he's streaking it for Roubideaux by now."

Then suddenly their mirth congealed on their lips. Three deep-toned and ominous reverberations shook the dug-out.

Bellew rushed outside.

"Good God!" he cursed. "He's blown up the tunnel."

He saw something moving down the creek.

"There he goes now," he cried. He sent a bullet speeding after the moving shadow.

"What's an honest man going to do with a skunk like that?"

In the early morning they viewed the results of the explosions. It would take several months to open the mine again.

Stannard's fortune was safe until the law could move.

CHAPTER
TWENTY-ONE

One Birdlike Note

Marcette gazed on Trois Riviers with a feeling of awe. She had never before seen so many houses together. Droulard's pocket-size edition of the department store of the big cities, as we know it, held her spell-bound. Many times she had received presents purchased therein.

Gaspard's, Minot's — she had heard of them, too. With Pierre, she trod the planked sidewalks feasting her eyes on the beautiful things displayed. The crudities and vulgarities of the little town were unseen by her.

She saw girls of her own years, some of them painted and rouged as if to advertise their age-old profession. Where a more sheltered girl would have beheld them in amazement, or shuddered at their business, she only lowered her eyes that they might not see the pity they awoke in her.

They seemed to be an inevitable part of the North. Even in far-off Roubideaux she had seen them. She proved herself the true Northern breed in that she pitied and not despised them.

MacNab had arranged lodgings for her. Pierre needed no one to care for him. He had found Luigi in a saner mood than was his wonted way. The old Italian became tractable at the sight of Pierre's gold pieces.

"All-a-right. We trya thees voice. *Deo mia*, I don't-a think I finda de voice in dis ice-box country. Come dis afternoon to La Roche's. We trya some leetla ting wid de piano."

The big dance-hall was deserted that time of the day. Old Peter had built it on piling over the rushing waters of the river. Age had kindly toned down its roughness. The suns of many summers had peeled off the paint on its railings and pillars where men had not previously carved their initials.

In a corner over the water the piano stood. For all its battered appearance the tone held. It shared the unenviable honor of being the only modern instrument of its kind in the town.

Luigi was there when Pierre and Marcette arrived. He eyed Marcette approvingly. At least he could see she was not flippant. There was a purpose about her that made the Italian smile. He knew the signs in these beginners. Years ago, before liquor had exiled him to the waste places, he had seen many of them rise to the top from the humblest beginnings.

He struck a chord or two and rubbed his hands.

"Now we trya the scale, so."

Marcette was ill at ease. She tried to remember what Diana had taught her, but in spite of herself her voice quavered. Luigi banged the piano.

"*Da capo, da capo,*" he repeated. "From de beginning again. Sing, don' watcha me."

Marcette did better that time. The Italian smiled. For half an hour they ran the scales until the full sweetness of those birdlike notes, which Diana had heard, rang in Luigi's ears.

"So," he smiled, "you can sing eef you will, eh? You knowa dat chanson, *'La Petite Rossignol'?* Well, we trya heem. All de voice dees time."

Marcette's courage had come back to her, and she let her voice out until it filled the empty room. When she had finished Luigi was all smiles. In spite of all his shortcomings and vices, music was his god. That he had stumbled upon a bit of genius delighted him as nothing else could have done.

"I guess you sing some day, maybe, eef you trya hard. But I don' understanda dat note — dat tone, I hear in your voice. You are only leetle girl, but I hear dat sadness — dat feeling a singer must have to be great. But which most of dem grow old before deya find."

Marcette beamed back at him. She knew he was pleased with her. As for Pierre Baptiste, it was something to be endured; but if it made Marcette happy, well enough.

Luigi gave her some exercises to practice and a talk about her breathing. It was not so different from the amateur lessons she had taken at Roubideaux.

"You come back every day for three, four day, at de same time, eh? We see what we do."

The hours did not hang heavy on their hands. Marcette was wrapped up in her lessons, and Pierre

164

was enjoying the first holiday he had known in over a year.

He it was who first discovered Stannard's presence. Jim was older and more haggard looking than he had seen him even during his sickness. For three days he avoided him and kept any mention of his name from Marcette.

Jim had not stopped at the Post. It held nothing for him now. His grub had run out before he reached Trois Riviers, so he arrived there in a terrible mood and fighting mad.

If the law failed him he did not know what he would do. A man could not keep up this battle against fate forever. When he had eaten and put himself in some sort of condition he went to see Lester, the lawyer.

He found Lazy seated on his front porch, a white-faced, contemplative Buddha. It was Stannard's presence in Trois Riviers that caused his thoughtfulness. He had seen him arrive. He remembered Jim from his long stay in the town the time he had first come into the North.

It furnished Lazy with an interesting problem. First, Ducet, Jim's partner, comes down river to file on another creek than the one on which he was supposed to be working; and now, right on his heels, came his partner. To Lazy's positive knowledge, they made no effort to find each other. Meaning a blow-up of some sort.

Stannard could not have guessed how timely his appearance was. But he only added to Lazy's mystery when he disposed of Pierre with a snarl.

165

"I don't know anything about the Mistageux. But I do know I would have held on to my mine, if he had not been a quitter."

Jim explained the mission that had brought him there.

Lazy invited him within. He acted as if he hated to do it. But these younger sons were a nuisance! What right had they to imagine they could come into a country and grab off a mine? He began his usual operation with the paper cutter as an aid to conversation.

"A sucker to be trimmed! He'll go home and marry the girl and talk all the rest of his life about the big chance he once had in the provinces."

That's what gouging the little finger-nail with the paper cutter said. Lazy put it differently.

"You see, the mining laws up here are strict, Stannard. If we didn't look out the Yankees would grab everything we have."

"But that group of claims on Windigo was held under the law by my father. He paid for the assessment work every year for five years," Jim said impetuously. The manicuring offended him.

"Paid for it, yes! But was it done? That's what you've got to prove. You can't do it, Stannard. For over two years the man, to whom your father sent the money for doing the annual work, was in the Klondike. He could not have been there and here, too. When he failed to do the necessary work before the first of the year, that threw the ground back to the government. The present owners re-located it."

"But I tell you" — began Jim hotly.

"Wait a minute," Lazy interrupted, juggling the paper cutter — "McGarvy's dead."

That seemed to clinch the argument in Lazy's eyes. He closed them in a slow, thoughtful, Buddha-like way, that suggested a benediction on the collector of assessments who had passed to the Hereafter without doing the work for which he had been paid. It carried with it also some regret at the frailty of human nature.

Jim champed like a blooded horse at the bit. For the first time in the young Englishman's life, he wanted to kick over the traces, to shoulder a gun and go out and fight the sheriff and his deputies for his property.

"They waited until I'd struck it rich before they thought much about McGarvy, or the assessment work, or anything else," he said grimly.

"Now, Stannard, the hall of records is right over there. Go there, and you'll see that a re-location notice on those Windigo claims was filed eighteen months ago or more."

"Look here, how do you happen to know so much about this matter?"

Something like a look of pity for the stupidity of this cold-foot crept into Lazy's eyes.

"I represent the Mannheim Syndicate, who have taken possession of their rightful property. And if you want my advice, I'd say, go back to England right away. They have never been known to lose."

With which remark Lazy poised the paper cutter as if about to attack the middle finger. To read sign — this

167

meant that an obstreperous person was in the way. He must be removed at an early date.

This conversation with Lazy seemed to apply the necessary lubricant to the chute down which Stannard elected to slide. Drink had never appealed to him as a surcease from worry. He tried it now, however, with astounding success.

It takes but a little while, in a place like Trois Riviers, for a man to slip far down the social scale if he is so minded. In three days he had reached the level where even the lumberjacks refused to hear his story, because they knew he did not have the price of a drink. He laughed.

"It's a rotten world," he mused. "A rotten old world. Not a decent man or woman in it."

He had wandered into Old Peter's place. He was spending the last of a dollar Nafferton had given him. Whatever differences had existed between them had floated away on the fumes of the whiskey with which he was saturated.

Everything seemed to have happened ages and ages ago — Pierre's desertion, the rush of the law and order at the mine, the appearance of that blond baby at Roubideaux. What did it matter now? Here was Nafferton, the rotter, the only man in the town who would lend him a dollar.

How he hated the whole mean business. He laughed again in his drunken, besotted way. He had not shaved in days. He was unlovely and ragged to a point where he little resembled the man he had once been.

Pierre had followed his descent with varied feelings. Times there were when he had difficulty in restraining himself from rushing to his side in an effort to put him on his feet. He knew they could not be friends again. The Englishman had violated all that friendship stands for by his attitude toward him. But it wrung his heart to see Jim rolling in the gutter this way. He was more than careful that Marcette should not come to know of it.

Marcette had not disappointed Luigi in that first promise of her ability. He was continually importuning Pierre to take her to Quebec or Montreal and give her a real chance.

"There is nothing a-more I can do for her, ma frien'," he said to Pierre. "Eef she have the courage she will-a be great some day. To-night I lika try something." Luigi turned to Marcette. "Your frien' he breeng you when da crowd is-a here. I feex it so Rosa, de girl what sing all-a the time, let you trya jus' one leetla song. Eef you do well, and don't get scare', I am sure you get the chance to go to Quebec."

Marcette turned to Pierre for confirmation of this.

"I don't know," he answered. "Me, I don' promise a t'ing. We wait and see. I know I can't go back to de Pos' and Père Vallois widout you. What he say eef he hear I let you sing 'for' all dese men and girls? Dis ees no place for nice young girl."

"That's-a true," Luigi answered for her. "As Dante said, 'Who enter here, leave all hope behind.' But you be safe, signorina, and it geeve me a chance to tell once for all eef you have the presence. So, you come then, eh? Luigi will wait for you by de leetla door."

Even Pierre, as close as he was to her, did not realize that this night was destined to swing her life one way or the other. It was never to be forgotten.

CHAPTER
TWENTY-TWO

"They Know Not What They Do"

Eight o'clock found standing room at Old Peter's long bar at a premium. Already the smoke hung like a pall about the large oil lamps. There was no room for a man without a penny in his pocket. Big Gabriel, Peter's bouncer, warned Stannard once and then started after him. Previous experience with Gabriel's boot, gained the evening before, accelerated his speed. He lurched across the dance-hall, which was still empty, and out on the long, porch-like room above the river.

Gabriel let him go. He was alone out there and out of the way. He lurched into a chair and sprawled head and shoulders over a table, his eyes rolling backward at the bright lights that had been denied him.

Back and forth his head rolled in an agony of weariness. The man had not slept since he had come to Trois Riviers. Since no one would listen, he talked to himself, mumbling brokenly a string of half articulated sounds which no one could have understood.

It was in this condition that Nafferton found him. He sat opposite him, gloating at the sorry spectacle before him. He laughed as he contemplated the wreck of what had once been a man. The proud, imperious Stannard was gone. Nothing but this groveling wretch, begging him for the price of a drink, remained. And he had accomplished it!

In his maudlin way Stannard tried to rise. Nafferton gave him a shove that sent him crumbling back in his chair. He wanted to enjoy this to the full.

For a week he had waited for some word from Bellew or Grace. Twenty-four hours after Stannard had arrived a messenger got in. From Lazy he learned the news of the blowing up of the tunnel and the information that it would be two months before they could re-open it. He could have killed Stannard for this.

Like a cat he kept out of Pierre's way, but when once Jim had begun to slide, he took a keen delight in helping him along to hell. As he watched him now he knew that the bottom had almost been reached. There remained the pleasure of parading him before the eyes of Marcette. He had kept that keenest delight for the last.

The ball-room had filled with a laughing, drinking crowd. Jim heard Luigi enter and open the piano. He could hear him talking to someone. Rosa, no doubt. Only a large window-like door separated them. The porch had no lights of its own, and from his rather dim retreat, he gazed at the gathering crowd.

Luigi struck a chord. He was sober to-night, and the happy-go-lucky crowd was quick to catch the masterly touch with which he played a Verdi overture. When he had finished a dozen invitations to have a drink were hurled at him.

A wait of a few minutes and they settled back to hear Rosa sob some sentimental ballad; but the girl who arose to sing was not Rosa. She was young and pretty. Had Old Peter pulled a surprise on them?

It was Marcette, trying to be calm and collected under Luigi's protection. He told her to forget the crowd and to sing for him alone. She heard him running over the introduction. It was only a simple little chanson. She opened her mouth and a birdlike note floated on the air. It was true and sturdy. It gave her immediate courage. The novelty and newness of the singer, as much as that beautiful tone, stilled the noisy crowd.

Note after note succeeded each other. It was a woodland melody — the pipe of a song sparrow. Luigi's hand lifted it to the dignity of a classic.

The voice so clear and pure awoke a sleeping memory in the poor wretch on the porch. He held his head up and listened. In some dim sort of way it sounded familiar. He got to his feet and staggered to the open door where he could see the singer. She was not ten yards away. He swayed as he caught sight of her. He clutched at the door for support. Nafferton peered over his shoulder.

"My God, Marcette!" Jim muttered in surprise. What was she doing in this dive?

Marcette had caught the movement by the door. The sight she beheld almost broke her down. Could this groveling, disheveled creature be Jim? As she sang she saw his curiosity turn to anger. Behind him she discerned the malignant face of Nafferton.

The song grew sad and mournful. The little sparrow was dying. Almost in a sob it ended, and that rough, case-hardened crowd yelled and stamped its approval, or wiped away a tear, depending on the sex of the listener.

Luigi bent and kissed Marcette's hand. He wished to add his tribute to her success. She had proved to him, beyond his wildest hopes, that she could reach the heart of an audience. It is the supreme gift of the singer.

The crowd trooped off for the bar. Only Luigi noticed the emotion that engulfed the girl. In amazement he watched her walk toward the door of the old porch and address the figure that leered at her from its shelter. Tears filled her eyes. She reached out her hands to help Stannard. All of her mother instinct had rushed to the surface. Gone was any recollection of injustice to Pierre.

"Jim," she implored, "M'sieu' Jim."

"Jim nothing," he snarled as he struck down her hands. He was nearer sober than he had been in days. "So it *is* you. This is where you've ended. The gutter next, eh?"

Even this did not stop her. She searched his eyes for some lingering ray of hope. The old debonnaire manner was gone. In its stead she saw that self-pitying, pathetic look the drunkard acquires when the world starts using him for a football.

She tried to humor him. She longed for Pierre to come.

"I warned you, Stannard," Nafferton sneered. "She's too damn pretty to go straight."

Something of the old fighting spirit flared back into Stannard's eyes. His jaw shot out as he turned on Nafferton. "You keep out of this, do you hear? I'll settle this affair."

He did not see the frightened Luigi hurrying away to find Pierre.

"Who brought you here?" he demanded of Marcette. "A singer in a cheap honkatonk! Answer me!"

Marcette bowed her head. Was there no end to the humiliation and insult that this man, of all men, could heap on her?

He bent close. The faint sweetness of her breath seemed to unnerve him. With unsteady hand he lifted her chin and looked into her eyes.

The feel of her flesh was maddening. He had suffered as few men have. Fate had played fast and loose with him for two years. But of all the agonies he had been called upon to bear none compared with this.

Here they were . . . he a drunken, penniless bum — she a singer in a cheap dance-hall. But as he looked into her eyes and felt that warm touch of her on his fingers, he knew that he loved her. He knew it as he knew it during the days when she had nursed him back to life. It was not of Cecilie he thought. She was of a remote age.

Now, in this cheap, theatrical atmosphere, he told himself the truth for the first time. He had loved her for

175

months. Thought of the promise he had given another had held him back. But now, when she was lost to him, the horrible truth would not be denied.

He knew he would have forgiven her her provincial clothes and ways. He would have taught her his own manner of life. And he knew why he had found speech impossible with Pierre.

This girl who had saved his life more than once, who had toiled and slaved for him, was taking her payment in full. As he stared at her, he knew his heart was being taken out and quartered. He could have killed Pierre Baptiste.

"You don't know what you are doing to me — you don't know what you are saying!" Marcette sobbed. "You don't! Pierre brought me here."

"Pierre!"

Stannard spat out the word as something unholy.

"I don't know, eh? Well, I do know that you, the girl I thought so pure and sweet, the girl I would have protected against any shadow of suspicion, are here in the toughest dive in Trois Riviers. You fooled me from the start with your lying eyes and lips. I know you lied to me about Aleekna's baby. You knew she was not the mother of it. You knew, by God, that Pierre was its father, didn't you — and that you were its mother?"

Under that awful blow Marcette sank to her knees.

"O — h — h — ! Merciful God, forgive him," she moaned.

Like a butcher standing over the lamb he has struck down, Stannard beheld her.

Came then a cry like the roar of a range bull. A giant dashed among them. With a bellow he knocked Nafferton under a table ten feet away. Picking Stannard up, he flung him into a chair with such force that it crumpled beneath him.

Tenderly he lifted Marcette into his arms. He held her as if she were a child.

"Never mind, my little one," he crooned to her in French. "I will take you far away from here — to Quebec. Don't cry."

He gave her to Luigi and turned to face the two men who had scrambled to their feet.

Nafferton would have slunk away had there been a chance, but Pierre filled the only doorway through which he could escape. The lust to kill was in the big Frenchman's eyes. Nafferton shrank into the corner. But the grim figure which had risen from the wreck of the chair, did not quail beneath the murderous eyes of Pierre Baptiste. He raised his hands as if to square off to fight. With a swing of his mighty paw Pierre sent him reeling backward.

Catlike he followed him up and helped him to his feet. Flat against the door jamb he pinioned him. It was as if Stannard were held in a trap. Jim started to speak. With the flat of his hand Pierre slapped him full on the mouth. The Englishman's head thudded against the wood.

"I talk now," roared the almost inarticulate Pierre. "You have talk enough for wan night. Now you lissen to me. I hear all dose dam' lies of yours. Now you hear de trut'. You know so much, eh? But you don' know dat

177

dat man, ees de fathaire of dat chil' — dat de mothaire ees your own sistaire! You don' know dat, eh?"

"No, no, Pierre," Marcette pleaded. "We promised he should never know."

"*Oui,*" he cried back at her. "I keep dat promise, even when he turns on me; but when he lays his han' on you — to hell wid dat promise."

From the corner of his eye he caught Nafferton drawing a gun. With a backward kick of his foot he sent it flying to the ceiling. He removed his hand from Stannard's shoulder. Let him fight now if he would.

Slowly comprehension came into the man's eyes.

"Diana — Nafferton?" He half whispered. Again and again he repeated it.

"It's a damned lie," Nafferton screeched as he saw Jim gathering to spring. "Why do they call him Pierre? Ask him that."

"You know why, M'sieu'," Marcette answered for Pierre. "Because the priest wanted to save the soul of that little baby, and Pierre stood up for him."

"Lies — lies!" Nafferton cursed. "It's a dirty trick to throw the blame on me."

"A trick, eh? Lak' de wan you use to steal his pocketbook. You snake, you *loup garou,* you steal ever't'ing he's got — his money, his mine, his sistaire — an' now his *honneur.*"

He turned back to Stannard.

"An' you," he ground out between his clenched teeth, "you pay us well for what we do for you, M'sieu'. But for her," and he pointed to Marcette — "but for her your bones would have rotted at Jacquard's Pass.

An' but for me you would have die on de creek. When no one else geeve a dam' 'bout you we have stan' by you to de las'. An' to pay us you try to keel de bes' wat ees in us."

Stannard's crucifixion was complete. From every pore in his body the clammy sweat ran. In a voice which he did recognize as his own, he spoke, but Pierre had not finished.

"Wan word more, den we go. Always you believe dat man dere. Even when de whole Nort' laughs at you. Show me wan man who don't know heem for a cheat an' a fake. But you tak' hees word. You let heem poison your min'. Eef you see Marcette here to-night, I ask you why? Who first fill her min' wit' dese idea? Who tell her she goin' be great singaire, some day? Your sistaire! Dat's who! Dat's why I bring her to Luigi to see eef she got a voice. Now I tak' her to Quebec where she don' have no frien' to mak' her cheap."

As Pierre raved on Nafferton slid his long, slender arm across the floor to where the pistol lay. His fingers had started to clutch it when a heavy boot came down on his wrist. Jim had seen the movement in time. He faced Pierre as he heard Nafferton groan in pain.

"M'sieur is right," he said in a dead tone. "It is even as you say. No time now for regrets or being sorry. A month from to-day the North will have forgotten that I ever lived. Grant me one last favor — close that door and wait outside. I want to settle this affair alone."

Before Marcette could interfere, Pierre had forced her and Luigi through the door and put his back to it. With a shove he sent the Italian to his piano. And the

179

returning crowd little guessed at the tragedy being enacted so near by. The giant Frenchman knew that the man had first right with Nafferton. It was the primal law.

Hardly had the door closed before Stannard caught the gun from Nafferton's fingers and sent it sailing into the river. With an angry cry the tortured man arose to his feet. About and about they circled in the moonlight on the porch.

Nafferton knew he fought for his life. Warily he ducked in and out of the flying fists that would have floored him had they sunk home. Suddenly he caught Jim with a wicked blow on the face. It brought blood. It ran into the corners of Stannard's mouth. The salty taste of it whipped him to a frenzy. He circled again until he had the river behind Nafferton's back. With a mighty lunge, then, he leaped at him. There was a crash and a sound of splintering wood. They both went down carrying the old, rotten railing with them. Nafferton screamed. He felt himself sliding over the porch into the foaming waters below. He dug his fingers into the flooring until his finger-nails broke off.

He clutched at Jim. Stannard felt himself slipping along with him. With all his strength he swung and caught his antagonist under the jaw. Nafferton's face went white. His grip relaxed and he went hurtling through the air to the boiling waters below.

Pierre had heard the ripping sound of the splintering wood. He pulled the door open and rushed in. Stannard was alone on the floor on his hands and knees peering down into the black waters of the angry river.

180

For an instant as he peered below there came the flash of a white, fear-stricken face. A gurgle and a last cry — then silence, and it was gone.

Pierre caught Stannard by the leg and pulled him back to the shelter of the door. The crowd gathered about them.

When they saw who had caused all the commotion, and that he lived, they let loose a torrent of witticism. "You couldn't drown an ole bum like that if you tried," one voice cried. "A fine guy, trying to break up a pleasant evening," his painted partner acquiesced.

Luigi got Pierre and Marcette to the back door and out to the street. Pierre half carried her home from there.

Before Marcette let Pierre go, she pleaded with him to find Stannard and see that the river did not claim him, too.

Pierre returned to La Roche's, but he did not find the man he sought. Jim was gone. Someone had seen him slink out of the bar-room half an hour ago.

Pierre walked the streets of Trois Riviers for an hour and visited every one of the saloons along the river's edge, but found no trace of Jim. When daylight came, he renewed his search. It brought no word of the man who had sent Nafferton to his doom.

CHAPTER
TWENTY-THREE

Oblivion

Two weeks after the disappearance of Jim Stannard from Trois Riviers, a ragged, ill-kempt tramp appeared in the little river towns of the lower Nishnibottni.

Folks were used to seeing his kind. Only this man did not tarry as the others did. A day or two and he was gone. From whence he came, or where he departed to, no one cared. This part of the North was used to the floaters who followed in the wake of the pulp cutters. They were an even more shiftless set than the lumberjacks they had known in the days of the big timber and hardwood.

By May, most of them had squandered all of their winter's wages. That was the month they usually appeared. This man was a full three months late.

Whenever he was fortunate enough to inveigle a riverman, or some brother derelict, with the price, into buying the drinks, he babbled a strange tale about a white face floating away on the river.

Facetious bartenders tried to twist him on his story, but without success. Peculiar how these wrecks always have some fanciful story of the past!

Pickings were poor for him, however. It was the wrong time of the year. His best audience had flown to the south at the first approach of summer. He even descended to the ignominy of a bar-fly, scrubbing and sweeping out place after place, that he might eat and drink. Even so, there came times when he was almost sober. Returning consciousness whipped him to a new effort to secure the precious whiskey that blotted out those awful memories.

His voice grew husky with the dampness of sleeping out nights. September was at hand, and the evenings were already growing cold. A brief Indian summer and then the cold rains would begin. It brought a twinge to the body of the man, but his mind was past caring. He welcomed death.

What was left to live for anyway? He had lost honor, friends, love, wealth. He cursed as the thought that God had made him in His image flashed into his befuddled brain. He was the ingrate — the great prodigal. Had a man ever been conceived who had repaid faith and kindness as he had done?

Day by day, in spite of himself, he reconstructed the past. He saw now how Pierre and Marcette had shielded him and tried to protect Diana. In sober moments, he recalled those last days on the creek. No wonder the Frenchman had deserted him.

And these were the people who even now cared for his sister's child.

Inevitably this train of thought led him to Nafferton. In one way or another, every misery that rested on him was traceable to the man he had killed.

He re-lived that night at Old Peter's. He heard the splintering railing. He saw again the pasty face of Nafferton as the river whirled him away.

The man had deserved his fate, but he had not meant to kill him; or else his white face would not have danced before him through all these days and nights.

By some miracle Nafferton might have escaped. Thus it was that Jim stuck to the river and sought the information no one could give him. At Bois Blanc a man had been washed ashore. He hurried there. A glance told him it was not the Englishman.

Thereafter he was not going anywhere. He had no destination; just the urge to keep on moving. There was no going back. That was his only definite fact. The North was closed to him forever.

There came no hint of the renewed misery his present whereabouts caused the girl he had shamed and humiliated. Yet it was evident that Pierre sensed the agony she was enduring as day followed day and no word came of Stannard.

MacNab agreed with the big Frenchman, when he had been taken into his confidence, that Marcette should go to Quebec.

"I've an auld-maid sister there who'll look after her and give her a proper home. André can dig into his sock a bit if needs be for the lassie. He'll roar like a bull for a while, but I'll tame him doon."

"De money don' worry me, MacNab. Eef you promise you feex eet with Père Vallois, I tak' her on de boat to Chambord to-morrow."

184

Marcette heard this decision with less happiness than she had ever believed possible. Quebec in itself was enough to frighten her, now that it loomed so close at hand. But the tragedy at Peter's, and Jim's fate dampened her enthusiasm like a wet blanket.

It was a long, tedious trip by lake and river to the little town where the railroad reached out a one-track branch of another branch that in itself was only a feeder to an unimportant division.

Pierre chose this opportunity to tell Marcette the truth about the Windigo. In liquid French he explained to her that mysterious filing of the claims on the Mistageux.

"Before I knew anyone had filed on the Windigo, I prospected that creek from end to end," he told her. "True, I see those old broken-down monuments, but years had passed since anyone had worked that creek. I never got a color there. So when Jim came along, I took him up the Mistageux. The summer before he came I had found traces there. He did not know one creek from the other. Nobody else did for that matter.

"And, too, I knew he would have great trouble holding onto his own claims if they did amount to anything. With all his papers gone, and no money to fight with, what chance did he have?"

"You mean," Marcette asked. "That this rich mine is not on the Windigo at all, and that it belongs to you and Jim?"

"*Vraiment, ma petite!*"

"Then you are both rich?"

185

"Bagosh," Pierre laughed and slid back into his patois. "We firs' got to prove what I say. Dat Mannheim crowd geeve us a beeg fight before dey geeve up. Dat's why I come to Trois Riviers P D Q. I smell de mouse. Nobody nevaire laugh at me."

"But Jim?" Marcette begged. "You must find him, Pierre. This news would brace him up. Luigi and you and I are the only ones who know about Nafferton. The man got what he deserved."

"You bat ma life on dat," Pierre assured her. "Eef he don' keel heem, I would."

"You and I know Jim was not responsible for his conduct. We cannot hold his awful words against him. He was crazy with drink and misfortune. You know that I have forgiven him. You will try and find him, won't you, Pierre?"

"For you I try, Marcette. I nevaire refuse you not'ing. Eef we don' fine heem we save hees share for dat leetle white hair Pierre at Roubideaux."

The thought of far-off home and her old, greying father made her lip quiver.

"I do not'ing 'bout de mine till Forrest, de surveyor from Ottawa, come next month. I know dat man ees hones'."

The little town they were bound for loomed in the distance. It made her homesick for the Post. If Pierre found Jim, and they recovered their mine, he would soon be off to marry the girl he had left in England. It was to be that way, though. She smiled grimly as she thought of Luigi. No wonder he had caught that note

186

of sadness in her voice. It had not come there by chance.

Marcette had never seen a train or a steam engine until that morning. The bustle which preceded its departure lifted her out of her moody thoughts. For the third time she made sure that her ticket and letters were safe.

Pierre talked to her through the window of the car. They were all French here, garrulous, talkative and bent upon their own farewells.

With a jerk the little train pulled out. From the platform he waved good-bye to her. She kept her tears until the train was beyond his sight. She knew Pierre well enough to know that the tears had not been far from his own eyes.

He waited there for two days before he started his long trek into the North. He was miserable without Marcette. His own sense of loneliness awakened within him a dull sort of sympathy for the man he had promised to find.

At times he doubted that Stannard lived.

Time softened Pierre's resentment against him. As he came into the North, and heard no word of Jim, he began to forgive him. He saw at last that the man had been sick mentally, even as one could be sick of body.

Once, when he had run down a well-founded clue without success, he berated himself for having first let Jim get away. As the rains came on he grew fearful of ever finding him.

Bit by bit he had worked his way up river until he found himself in the pulp country. For miles on either side of the river, the poplar was being snaked down to the mills and ground into paper pulp.

In the spring when the loggers were in the woods it would have been a likely place to have looked, but Pierre knew they were not cutting now. Nevertheless it was a chance. So he searched out the old camps.

About the time that Pierre had left Chambord, Stannard had shown up at Presque Isle.

Saturday night was the big night there. The Continental Pulp Mills owned the town. An old narrow-gauge road ran back into the hills from the mill. Over its rusty rails the wild, ribald crew, who were whooping it up this night in Dennis Sweeney's bar-room, brought the popin, cut the winter before, and which lay beyond the spring water-head.

They were raising the roof to-night. Occasionally a lull came. It was the preliminary to an outburst of denunciation — the quick rush of a body through the air and the sight of Dennis standing foursquare between the swinging doors.

He stood there now regarding the latest victim, the luckless Stannard.

Sweeney was a mighty man among this crowd of Swedes, Souwegians and Galway Irish. The man tried to rise from the wet sawdust to which he had been consigned by the Sweeney foot. Dennis let him have it again.

There seemed to be a mute acceptance of this decision as final: silence followed.

188

Sweeny turned toward the bar. The crowd made a passageway for him. They knew the incident was closed. Nowhere was it on record, that there had ever been a come-back to one of these encounters.

The Englishman was evidently not acquainted with local history. For, after an interval of ten minutes, he got to his feet and rushed blindly through the swinging doors.

Sweeney saw him coming. The second encounter was even briefer than the first. A right to the jaw knocked Stannard cold. But for his last second's clinch, he would have been down to the floor where the Sweeney feet would have been used with undisputed results.

The leg Stannard had caught at to keep himself from falling belonged to Ole Jacobsen, the cook of the outfit. Sweeney tried to pull him loose. Jim turned a beseeching face to Ole. He knew what the Sweeney feet could do.

The silent, shut-mouthed Swede was well liquored. He held no love for the Irish. The derelict's appeal to him for protection was the needed fuel to make him stand up before Sweeney.

He pushed him back and swung a heavy chair high above his head. "Ya," he roared. "You let dis feller alone!"

The crowd drew a circle about them.

"Aye ban take him away!"

Sweeney unclenched his fists.

"Take him, you squarehead. Get him out of here or I'll break him in two."

189

"Ya," Ole laughed. "Aye ban villin' see you try. You hit him, aye skoll fight. Aye ban veigh two hundred saxty pound, Arishman."

Diplomatically Sweeney left the cracking of this nut for another time.

"All right, Ole. Get him out. Look where he scratched me face."

The cook lifted Stannard to his feet as the crowd drew back to the bar.

The camp was four miles out in the bush. To get to and fro the men used the two or three old hand-cars which the company owned. The Swede headed up the road to where they sat on the track.

Without ceremony he dumped Stannard on to one of them and rolled away into the hills.

When Jim awoke the next morning Ole stood over him. It was still grey dawn. A heavy mist hung over everything. The trees dripped from the rain of the night before. Near at hand the smoke from the cook-fire arose, white and heavy.

Salt pork, beans, bread and black coffee greeted him. It was rough, coarse fare, but in abundance.

Ole made no mention of the night before. When sober he rarely spoke. Unbidden, Stannard turned to the pots and pans. He had eaten. Hence it followed that he must toil. There he stuck. It was his first anchorage in months.

Like a hound he followed Ole — always at that interval of a step. Even in the North, where castes are not supposed to exist, it marked the difference between them. It said that one served the other.

190

Servile, beaten, his lustreless eyes holding no hope of the future, he scrubbed Ole's pots and washed his clothes.

And to this camp in the poplars came Pierre Baptiste.

CHAPTER
TWENTY-FOUR

No Braver Thing

When Stannard saw the big Frenchman bearing toward him his first inclination was to run. He had thought pride dead in himself. But he sensed now a feeling of shame that he should see him. He wiped the greasy suds from his hands and arms and raised his eyes until they met Pierre's.

He wondered what the man could want of him. Had they found Nafferton? Was the law after him? Or did he come to even the old score between them?

But Pierre stretched out his hands to him.

He heard him talking — saying he was glad he had found him; that he had searched for him for weeks.

It was incredible. But bit by bit the conviction sank home that he had come to help him. Could it be possible that he still had a friend?

Ole called to him to get on with his work. Automatically he jumped, and sank his arms into the tub.

Pierre pulled him back as Ole's eyes bulged.

"Non, non, Jim," he said. "Our Swede frien' can wash hees own deesh. You come wit' me."

192

Ole cursed as they swung aboard the log train bound for the mill. "Ya ban take dam' goot feller 'way from Ole," he cried at Pierre.

Pierre waved his hand at him. His long search was over.

Subconsciously Stannard knew that he was taken to town and re-clothed, and properly fed and rested. The scraggy beard and old rags removed, he presented a different appearance. But it became an increasingly more difficult matter to awaken in him the old fight, the desire to win back what he had lost.

With little interest Jim heard Pierre's story of the Windigo, and that he had filed on the other creek. No one had ever heard of Nafferton. Nobody seemed to regret or to be interested in his disappearance.

They remained at Presque Isle for a week. Patiently Pierre doled out the whiskey to Jim. It was like weaning a baby. But he knew he had won. Purposely he witheld information that might arouse the man's curiosity and awaken his anxiety. His plan began to work. Stannard asked questions. How did Pierre propose to wrest his property from the powerful interests now in possession of it?

"What are you going to do — how do you propose to get it back?" he questioned.

Pierre commenced to think he might be successful.

"What you goin' to do?" he retorted. "Eet's jus' as much yours as eet ees mine. When we start, you say feefty-feefty. Well, we still be feefty-feefty."

Here was a man whose word was his bond. There was some good in the world at that. It put something of

193

the old snap in Jim's under jaw. He began to relish the prospect of the fight that loomed before them.

"We'll make a try for it, Pierre, if you say the word. We have the money to do it with, if we can reach it. Before I left the creek I got out a pocket of the real quill, and cached it in one of our four holes — it ought to run close to a hundred thousand. We can fight them to kingdom-come with that."

While they waited and planned their attack, the Ariel, Forrest's white launch, came chugging along and tied up at the mill wharf. Between now and the time snow fell, he and his men intended to run a survey through unchartered country between the Nishnibottni and the Misstassini. The rush into the Copper Kettle country next spring would make it imperative.

Pierre succeeded in placing on Jim's shoulders the responsibility of laying the case before the surveyor.

He found Forrest an agreeable surprise. He was unlike the other government officials he had come in contact with. His hair had grown white in the years he had passed in the North, which he loved and did so much for.

He beamed at Jim when he mentioned Ducet.

"The best the North can produce," he asserted. "I've known of him for years. There isn't a wrong bone in his body."

"I can vouch for that," Stannard hastened to answer. "I told him I had cached enough gold to give us a fighting stake if we could get it out. He seemed to think you might see a way to prove our rights in the case without going into the courts."

"He is wise to keep away from the courts with that crowd. Pierre knows the country better than any white man in the North. If these people have filed on your property on the Windigo, and the mine is on the Mistageux, then they are trespassing. I know the Windigo well enough. In fact we used it for our base line when we ran the original survey. The two creeks enter the river at almost the same spot, but the Windigo bears off to the eastward more."

"That's exactly how Pierre described it."

"Well, I'd take his word," the surveyor assured him. "The Mistageux is only half the size of the other creek. I christened it myself, out of courtesy to the morning we ran it. The thing for you to do is to get there in a hurry. Possession is nine points of the law the way the Mannheim crowd play the game and it will work the same way for you. We will be ready to leave here in an hour. Suppose Pierre and you get your stuff aboard. We can talk it over as we run along. I've got a good six weeks' work ahead of me up there."

Needless to say, both Pierre and Jim were delighted with the promise of help the official had given them. That night in his cabin they carefully planned the recovery of the mine.

Forrest believed that it would be wisest to slip through Trois Riviers at night. The town abounded in spies who would rush to Lazy with the news that they were headed for the creek. Forrest had five men with him, fellows he could depend on, but they would not be a handful to the gang Lazy would send after them, were he sure of their destination.

The Ariel had been used to hunt poachers on the Great Lakes before Forrest acquired her. Her old speed remained. He knew they would pass Trois Riviers the next night. From there, with luck, they should make the Post in four days. Unless they were forced to stop, another three days would see them as far up as the boat could go.

Health flowed back into Stannard's veins. With delight Pierre saw the old eagerness and fire come into the eyes of the man he was so closely bound to. By the time they left the boat Jim was beginning to resemble the man he once had been.

From the hill in back of the dug-out they reconnoitered the ground. Someone dozed beside the door. It was Bellew, the deputy. No one else was in sight.

Forrest gazed up and down the creek with the sure recollection of previous acquaintance.

"No question about it," he said positively. "This is the Mistageux. The creek we forded two miles back was the Windigo. You can see where they join the river from this rock."

"The best thing to do now is to follow this ridge up creek for a quarter of a mile. We'll be able to see the shaft from there. If the men are working it someone will be at the windlass."

Pierre agreed with Jim on this.

"Bes' of all we can cross de creek dere wit'out bein' seen from de dug-out," he said.

Forrest said that the wisest thing to do was to surprise the men if possible. Bellew, the deputy, held an

196

ambiguous position. Forrest knew that he was a Mannheim agent, but whether he would get off when he knew the truth, and saw it backed up by government men, or refuse, was a question.

When Pierre had led them to a point of vantage they saw, as he had predicted, a man idling by the windlass. By the look of things Grace had the old shaft and tunnel about opened. Another half hour and the men would be coming up for the day.

Pierre got across first. Before Forrest was out of the water the Frenchman had advanced to a point where he could have jumped on the man by the windlass. When he knew his companions were near enough to come to his aid if necessary, he did jump. He carried the man down with him. The suddenness with which the wind was knocked from him left the fellow stunned. One of Forrest's men tied him up.

In a few minutes there came a tug on the windlass rope and a voice hollered to pull away. Pierre and one of the rod men turned the windlass with a will. The surprised look that crossed the face of the man standing in the ore bucket was ridiculous.

One by one they reeled them up and bound them. Grace was the last. Jim spared him that indignity.

"The tables are turned this time," he greeted the engineer. "It's your birthday this trip."

Grace recognized Forrest. He nodded to him.

"What's the meaning of this, anyhow? Have you got anything to do with it?"

"Well, I'll tell you, Grace, how it is. Your people have been roped in. This surprise party is not my doing entirely, although I acquiesced in the matter, because from past experience I have found your crowd slow to withdraw even when you were in the wrong."

"How are we in the wrong? We have recorded these claims here on the Windigo. I have the papers in the dug-out this minute."

"When you show me those papers I'll prove to you just where you are wrong. Ainsworth, you stay here with these men. The rest of us will go have a look at the dug-out."

Bellew went for his gun when he saw them coming. When he recognized that they were government men he straddled the fence, waiting for Grace to give him his cue.

With a flourish Grace threw the copies of the filings and entries on the table. Forrest read them hurriedly as he produced a map and spread it before the astonished engineer.

"Now, Grace, take a look. Where that pencil is is where your claims lie. Here is where you are," and he moved the pencil ever so slightly. "You are on the wrong creek. This is the Mistageux. It's two miles on a bee line from here to the locations called for in those filings."

He proceeded to relate how he had met Jim and Pierre, and why he was in the country.

"I ran this survey and I know what I'm talking about. You people have been trespassing and holding this property from its rightful owners. The manner in which you jumped it riles my blood. I don't know how you'll come out down below, but I have the authority to arrest you and I'm going to do it."

"You're goin' pretty fast there, ain't you Chief?" Bellew asked. "I got a court order to hold this property. You can't arrest me."

Without a word Jim turned and gave Mr. Bellew one straight from the shoulder. Before he recovered his own handcuffs dangled from his wrists. Jim smiled at him.

"I guess we are quits now, Marshal — what?"

"Yer dam' fresh about it, anyway," Bellew answered sullenly.

"Well, what about you, Grace?" Forrest asked. "Are you going to cause any trouble or are you going to go along peacefully?"

"Where do you propose taking us to?"

"The Ariel is below the rapids. You'll walk that far to-morrow. I'll ride you all as far as Roubideaux and see that you go south from there in irons. Once you hit Trois Riviers you'll be out on bail in ten minutes. Old Lazy will get Colburn up from Montreal on this, no doubt, but I fancy that when I have talked to him he will lay off of this deal."

Before it grew dark Jim and Pierre unearthed the treasure that he had cached. Pierre's eyes widened as he gazed upon it.

"*Mon jee,*" he whistled. "More lak' eet bee two hundred t'ousand dollaire here. I tole you how eet be when you find heem."

That night the dug-out resembled the evening Jim had knocked the beef-tin to the floor. Bellew grinned as he told him how they had framed his escape for him.

Jim laughed, too. He could afford to laugh to-night. They had recovered the mine without a shot being fired. Best of all, Forrest had volunteered to leave two of his men behind to guard the claim. Even the Syndicate would be slow about running off government men.

After months and months of misfortune and failure luck had smiled on him at last. England loomed near at hand. How quickly fate can change the cards. A month ago he had forgotten there was such a place as home.

But as the thought of England grew there came another to pierce him to the heart — Marcette.

Not once since Pierre had found him had her name passed the lips of either. Thought of her made England seem less inviting. He had not heard from Cecilie in months. Yet he knew he would fulfill his promise to her. And the man who had so lately laughed at the twist by which fate had heaped riches into his lap, now berated that same fate for making such a mess of life.

Even now, as if by mutual consent, both he and Pierre avoided the subject of Marcette. It was as if both realized that the book was closed. And yet Stannard would have suffered the tortures of the Inquisition to have erased from her mind the memory of that night at Trois Riviers. No matter what the future might bring, happiness, he knew, ended here, for him.

CHAPTER
TWENTY-FIVE

Poor Little
Song Sparrow

A subdued and quiet Roubideaux greeted them. Smallpox had come with the rains. Every third year it was the same. It mowed down the Nascaupees in dreadful numbers.

The Factor was disconsolate. Old Aleekna, and the little blond Pierre, had been snatched away with the first. At the hint of its coming there had been a mad rush to get out.

Valiantly, the little priest had fought the scourge to a finish. For strange reasons, some might have thought, he placed the child beside the grave of the dead English girl. And yet one hears it said that there is no sentiment in the North.

Naturally the Factor blamed all of the misfortunes which had befallen him on the mad rush for gold.

"It is the cause of it all," he reiterated. "Until it maddened these people, we were happy. We had plenty of room. We fought disease when it came. We had obedient children. The North was unspoiled and fit to live in. Look at it now!"

Jim took the news of the child's death stoically. In many ways he realized it was for the best.

Forrest's time was too precious to allow him any to waste. He arranged with MacNab to turn the prisoners over to the authorities in Trois Riviers. Pierre and Jim both intended going down with the Captain. Forrest had obligingly given them a letter to a friend in Quebec, who, he thought, would be willing to undertake the management of the property.

Jim had determined to go back to England at once. Pierre had tried to dissuade him, but Stannard would not listen. He owed it to Cecilie. And besides, London *did* beckon to him. In all the years he had been away he had not lost, for any length of time, his oft-repeated longing for the luxuries he craved. That they needed an experienced man to work the mine, and safeguard their interests, was evident.

With a deep feeling of gratefulness, they bade God-speed to the surveyor as he headed back for the creeks. Forrest would not accept a cent for all he had done for them. He, and a few like him, made the North what it is to-day.

"You better come 'long, Père Vallois," Pierre beseeched the Factor. "Jim an' me soon git done wit' business. I see him off an' den Marcette an' you an' me have a real holiday. I bat we don' know dat girl now. Bagosh, pretty soon I have money enough to build my own opera house for her."

Pierre's wide, diplomatic smile could not move André. He was not the traveling kind. MacNab's tales of the changes down river disgusted him.

"No, my friend, I stay here. A Factor's place is at his post during the long winter. I'll have trouble enough equaling last year's record even if I stay at home. You tell Marcette Père Vallois is waiting for her. When the spring comes I want her to come home. It's very lonely here without my little songbird."

MacNab, the canny Scot, was the most cheerful one of them all. He had fancied Jim from the start, and now that he was rich, he took pride unto himself for having foreseen his success.

MacNab knew more about that night at Peter's than he would admit. Safe to say, that he knew the depths from which Jim had climbed.

Old Lazy's eyes popped as he beheld Grace and his cohorts marched off to jail. He had them out on bail in less time than Forrest had said. Jim doubted that they would ever be brought to trial. He had promised Pierre he would return in the spring, if his presence were needed in court, but the sad-eyed Frenchman had little hope that even this contingency would bring Stannard back.

His guess had been nearest correct in the matter of the ore Jim had cached. For the first time in his life Pierre had a bank balance. Impatiently he faced the trip to Quebec. He was hungry for a sight of Marcette. That she could be kept out of their conversation much longer was impossible.

Jim felt this first. He knew Pierre would not be in the city an hour before he would be off to find her. It drove any thought of Duncan, Forrest's friend, far from his mind.

A dozen times he tried to broach the subject of Marcette to Pierre, but turned away from it invariably. Jim knew he would have a two days' wait for his ship to sail. He tried to tell himself that the best thing to do would be to go straight to Marcette and try and beg her forgiveness for the terrible past. But that seemed so futile — so like opening an old hurt without being able to heal it.

He tried to picture Marcette as she would be now. He knew the change in her must be great. How he would have loved to be able to go to her on the old understanding!

He was going home, and yet even now he was strangely homesick for the things he was leaving so soon. How differently he would have felt were Marcette going back with him. Down in his heart he knew he would have been happy to have had her even as she had been in the past for all her primitiveness.

Had he been blind that he had not seen the love and faith this girl had had for him? He sank his teeth into his lips as he thought of his past imbecility. He berated himself for the blindness of youth that had closed his eyes.

And yet, these were strange thoughts for a man going home to wed another.

As England and Cecilie flashed into his mind, he knew that he could not face Marcette. His very leaving would only seem another proof of his unworthiness.

They would be in Quebec to-morrow evening. It became necessary now, no matter what the cost, to tell

Pierre how he felt. When he spoke the big man's face fell.

"All de tam', Jim, I been look to de day when we all be togethaire. You break her heart for sure eef you don' see her. I tell you Marcette forget all 'bout dat night at Peter's. Eef not, why she mak' me fine you?"

"I'd rather die than look into her eyes and see the hurt that I had placed there," he answered. "A woman does not forget these things, Pierre."

"Some women, ma frien," Pierre replied forlornly.

Talk got them nowhere. Impatiently Jim opened his heart to the man who had done so much for him. "If I had anything but empty words to offer her, I would crawl to Marcette on my hands and knees and beg her forgiveness. But Nafferton spoke the truth when he said I was promised to a girl back home. I am — a boyhood romance. Maybe I have outgrown it. But I know I would be less than a man if I failed to keep my word with that girl."

Over a year ago he had told him the same thing. Pierre had not forgotten that night in the dug-out on the creek. Gloom settled down upon them as they made the long trip by train from Chambord.

"But you come back some day to Canada, Jim?" Pierre pleaded.

"Maybe, Pierre. The future is all clouded for me. I've got all I came for now. And yet I'm unhappy. Seems that I've lost more than I have gained. Once I am home that will pass away, no doubt. But no matter where I go, Canada will call to me some day. And you — Pierre

205

Baptiste — you're the salt of the earth. I won't forget you."

He squeezed the big fellow's knee as he gazed out of the car window.

Pierre blew his nose violently as a protest but before they reached Parent Square station he had promised that he would not see Marcette until Jim had sailed.

Jim had wired Duncan to meet them that evening at the Frontenac. He was waiting when they arrived.

The sight of these adventurers from the far North caused a stir in the big Château. They had a late dinner served in their rooms and went over their business with the mining man. Stannard liked the curve of Duncan's fighting jaw. Forrest had evidently made no mistake in his choice of man.

After he left Jim explained a proposition to Pierre that had been in his mind for some time.

"I don't know how you will feel about it," he began. "But it seems to me that we ought to incorporate. I am going away, and you will not want to spend the rest of your life working the property. Duncan seems like the right man for us, but it will take something more than a salary to hold his interest forever."

"I do anything you want, Jim, you know dat."

Stannard paused before he went on.

"And there is one thing more. Coming from me alone, it would be refused; but from both of us, it hardly could be — what I mean is, that I want Marcette to have an equal share with us. It's no more than her due. Without her help — well, you know — we don't need to go into that. What do you say?"

206

All Pierre could do was to stare at his friend who sat watching the crowd moving along Dufferin Terrace. He crossed over to where Jim sat. Almost affectionately he placed his huge arm about Stannard's shoulders."

"You would do dat much for her, eh, Jim?" he finally asked.

"So little, you mean, I guess," he replied. "Of all that I should do, that is the least."

It meant that Marcette would be a millionairess in her own name some day.

When Duncan returned in the morning he brought with him a counsellor-of-law whom he could recommend. He was delighted with the good news that awaited him. Noon-time came before they had finished.

Pierre agreed to wait in Quebec until the legal arrangements had been completed and Duncan had arranged for the necessary machinery. Then they would return together.

There began then an orgy of spending by both Jim and Pierre. The steamer would sail by ten o'clock the next morning. It gave Stannard little enough time to purchase the many things he needed.

He laughed and despaired as he saw Pierre's flair for the decorative soar to the skies. Everything was new to the big man. Until the previous evening he had never seen a motor car or telephone, a street car or a movie. Like a full-grown Alice, he had arrived in Wonderland. It never occurred to him to be frightened as Jim had thought it would. Everything was marvelous. Men waited on him hand and foot to his great enjoyment, his huge tips working havoc among the other guests.

207

Jim left him alone that evening, on his strict promise not to leave the hotel until he returned. It was just the opportunity the reporters had waited for. The truth about the newly made millionaires had gotten beyond the doors of the hotel.

When Jim returned he found Pierre surrounded by a group of newspapermen to whom he had unburdened his soul. Jim could do nothing but admit the facts.

The morning papers carried variously garbled accounts of their rise to wealth. Spread over the front page of the Journal was an immense picture of Pierre and his three-carat pin.

Jim arose at an early hour to get his luggage aboard ship. A glance at the papers and he became panicky. It was not to be supposed that Marcette would fail to learn of their presence in town, now.

An hour before sailing time he went aboard. Everywhere they went they were recognized.

With beating heart Marcette read the story. It was her first knowledge that Pierre had found Jim. The recovery of the mine and their presence in Quebec was as new to her as to the most disinterested reader.

Stannard would hardly have recognized her. Already the refining influence of the Ursuline sisters was beginning to tell. There was a new grace in her walk, a cosmopolitan flavor to her speech.

Tears dimmed her eyes as she realized that Jim had fought his way to the top. The hurt in the knowledge that he was sailing, even then, for home, was as nothing to the joy she felt in his regeneration.

Like one in a trance she dressed and climbed to the heights above the St. Lawrence.

So it was that Pierre, dashing to her address from seeing Jim off, found her gone. Impatiently he sank back into the cushions of his hired motor to wait until she returned.

As the last fold in the hills above Montcalm's City straightened out and became an indistinct blur, the lonely man pacing the decks of the big liner would have given his soul to have known that she was there on the Plains of Abraham watching him go out of her life.

If only by a miracle she could send him some word, or signal, that she had forgiven him!

And as the liner dipped against the horizon the signal came.

On bended knees, Marcette prayed:

"God keep you, my Jim, and bring you back to me some day."

CHAPTER
TWENTY-SIX

The Lure of Little Voices

Among the wraith-like figures hurrying through the fog ten days later to catch the Charing Cross bus or a Fleet Street taxi was one, tall, well proportioned and sun-browned. He stepped aside at the door of the University Club.

It was Jim Stannard on his way to meet Manning. In a detached, impersonal way he stood on the steps and watched his fellow ghosts glide noiselessly through the mist that enveloped London in a yellow shroud.

He was in it, but not of it. Memories of Marcette haunted him. Something vital to life was missing.

This conviction had been growing on him gradually for a month. Stannard had tried his best to settle down to the routine of the life he had left behind two years before.

From the moment he had caught the fogs in the Irish Sea his spirits had risen. The coast of Devon had thrilled him with its beauty. No home-sick prodigal had ever returned with a more hungry heart for his native land.

England had not changed, but his friends had. Money, now that he had it in quantities, seemed unable to buy him the happiness he had always felt denied him for lack of it.

He had found a note from Cecilie at his Club in answer to his cable telling her he was arriving. It was the first thorn in his home-coming.

It was an awkward note to write, inasmuch as she had been married for three months. True to his type, he would have married her, had she waited, no matter what the cost to himself. He had smiled as he destroyed the letter. At least he was foot-loose.

He started then a round of pleasure such as he had dreamed of, but try as he might, he could not find the old values. The men were a dawdling, afternoon-tea-drinking, polo-playing crowd.

To the women of his set, he tried to be merciful. He found that sincerity was something to smile at indulgently; ideas, an amusement — to be used as the small change of thought.

What was it all about, this coming and going, this dressing and still more dressing? He could not move without a tape measure.

He was sick of it. It was all drivel. All vanity and vexation of spirit. No wonder Cecilie had not waited for him.

He found Ken in the smoking room.

"You're not looking fit, old man," was his friend's greeting. "What's happened?"

"I hardly know, Ken. It seemed out there in the fog that I'd got a minute of insight, or something. You know, one of those illuminating pauses that come to everybody."

"Rot, I call that introspective stuff," Denkin, the club pest, interrupted. "Let's have a drink, what?"

"I'll meet you in the bar," Ken said. "I'll get tickets for 'The Love Girl' or something light, to cheer you up."

"If you insist," Jim called to his friend.

"I'm sick of teas and theatres," he said to Denkin. "I'd rather spend the evening here."

"Your digestion's bad, that's all," the wit answered. "You are not the conventional prodigal. By the way, did you ever meet Nafferton out there?"

Stannard blanched and shook his head.

All through dinner he was over-reserved.

From their table Jim looked out on what seemed to him an unreal world. The noiseless, shadowy shapes, that moved swiftly past the window blended in with the purr of the great city awakening for its nightly revel.

The club was almost deserted by the time they got to the coffee. Pleasure and happiness seemed always to be somewhere else. An hour from now would find the men who had dined there spread all over London seeking adventure of one sort and another.

Ken called the taxi and they sped off for His Majesty's Theatre. It was a stupid review. The girls were pretty enough; but the comedy inane to Jim.

During the intermission he begged off, and they drove back to the club for a game of billiards and a chat.

It was well toward midnight when Ken ventured on a subject that had not been mentioned since Jim's arrival in England. The meeting was to dispose of it, so far as he could manage.

"A man's affections play a large part in his moods and his life," Manning said thoughtfully.

"A big part."

This was more help than Ken expected. He went on.

"I don't want Cecilie's marriage to hold you back — You know, aloof from us, Jim. And I'm sorry it turned out this way."

For a while the faint murmur of voices, with now and then an exclamation and a loud laugh from the table where Denkin was seated, was his only immediate answer.

"My dear, Ken," Jim finally said, "I want you to know that I don't hold it against her. Two years is a long time for a girl to wait."

Ken leaned forward.

"You're all right, Jim. I'm proud of you; proud of what you have done; proud of what you are trying to do. But I can't help feeling that Cecilie treated you rather shabbily."

Jim was in a quandary. He did not want to hurt his friend by telling him that only a sense of duty had held him true to his boyish allegiance to Cecilie. At the same time he wanted to play fair with himself.

"Look here, Ken," he said, "you may as well know, Cecilie's marriage did give me a twinge. But I'll get on."

"Really?"

"I'm telling you the truth."

"No! You're just saying that to keep us from feeling badly at home."

"Listen, Ken. I'm just admitting it now, but I've known this since my first week in England. I'd be sorry if any chain bound me here. Cecilie's marriage gave me a shock, but it gives me a sense of freedom."

"Can you say that?"

This was offered with something of a hurt tone.

"Don't misunderstand me, Ken. I love England and its traditions. I have only the kindest feelings for Cecilie. But this country is no longer mine; its people are alien to me."

"But your friends?"

"One's friends are that, from year to year, only as they grow with one. How will I say what I want to say without appearing to put on side? It's not that I've done anything in particular to be proud of — it's because you have done nothing, er . . . not even tried. You are in a treadmill over here of social teas and company dinners. It keeps you from thinking. Worse than that, it keeps you from getting in touch with the things that induce thought."

"You're not going back to the Provinces — you are not hinting at that?"

A far-away look came into Jim's eyes. Roubideaux was lifted against the background of the interminable wastes. Again he was on the deck of the *Morning Mist;* the old Factor was standing on the wharf; Marcette was snuggled against him. They were waiting for the first news from the outside after the long winter. Always

214

master of his emotions among his unemotional kind, Jim answered quietly:

"I guess I'll be going back, Ken. Yes . . ." He nodded his head sagely . . . "I'll be going back some day."

CHAPTER
TWENTY-SEVEN

The Wings of
the Moth

While Stannard tarried in London, spring came again to Canada and the North. The wild geese found a changed land this year. Trois Riviers had grown in size and wickedness. Roubideaux had become a town. A dozen boats were waiting to plough their way up the river where once the *Morning Mist* had reigned supreme.

From his porch in Trois Riviers, old Lazy gazed with interest on the busy carpenters, who, overnight it seemed, were erecting a combination theatre, dance-hall and saloon, that made Old Peter's place fade into insignificance.

Directing the crowd of workmen was one who particularly engaged Lazy's interest. Ten months had made a change in the man. He was older, thinner, and his hair greyed about the temples. But there was jauntiness in him, an air of authority and prosperity quite new.

It was Nafferton, back from the grave to which Lazy had long ago consigned him. His travels and occupations had been many and varied in the time since he had fallen screaming into the river. Clutching the railing he had carried away with him in his descent, he had been whirled down stream to the big eddies at the Death Chute. Once caught in the whirlpools the old railing had broken to kindling as it came into contact with the heavy logs caught there momentarily. He had fastened on to one of these before it shot out of the eddy with express-train speed.

Ten minutes later, Charlie Pine, a Montagnais half-breed, had pulled him out of the back-water more drowned than alive. Charlie had been fishing from a sand spit, which ran out into the river, when he had seen Nafferton floating by.

The Englishman made no immediate attempt to return to Trois Riviers. When he heard of the swindle he had helped to perpetrate on the Mannheims, it became Nafferton's ambition to put as much distance as he could manage between Trois Riviers and himself. That Lazy would ever forgive him for the unconscious fraud he had worked was beyond the possibilities. His life wouldn't be safe until he had returned the money he had been given by the Mannheim agent.

Why Pierre had not forced the attack on him also worried Nafferton. Between Stannard and the Frenchman revenge, of one sort or another, was sure to overtake him if he tried to return.

Somewhere, far to the south and west he knew there was a crossing where the trails north from Kamshigama Lake and south from Fort Revillac intersected. He arranged with Charlie to take him there. His route from the crossing took him south to the railroad and eastward to Quebec.

Once there, Nafferton had turned to anything to make both ends meet. Petty gambling and one or two shady deals had put him back on his feet. As he waxed strong in his new haunts he never for a minute lost his touch with the things of the North. With hatred and envy he read the newspaper stories about Pierre and Jim. He even tried to find Marcette.

With Stannard in England, Nafferton's return to the North awaited only his squaring himself with Lazy. Events had cleared him of any suspicion of having tried to double-cross the man.

In Quebec he had gathered about him a choice band of cut-throats. They constituted his bodyguard against all aggressors.

At the first hint of spring he had gathered his forces and headed for Trois Riviers. Lazy once mollified, he walked the streets with freedom, putting off with a wave of his hand any one whose curiosity had been aroused by his return.

With a flourish and a blare of brass, he flung open the doors of the most ornate establishment in the North. Craps, faro, roulette, stud — all of the devices a new country knows for extracting money from full pockets blossomed forth at his direction. The coarse, hardened women, who had held forth at La Roche's, found themselves out of favor beside the youth and beauty he had brought with him.

218

Up and down the river the news of Nafferton's place flew. Prosperity to marvel at was his. What Skagway had been to the Klondike, Trois Riviers became to the Copper Kettle — the gateway to the gold country. And over its infamy there hung, like a bird of prey, the depraved, vicious spirit of this man who basked so securely in the smiles of his satellites.

Like a messenger of the devil, suave, flattering, patronizing, he moved among the crowds that nightly came his way, his sardonic smile never failing him. And drawn hither, like the moth to the flame, came the luckless Mr. Muldoon who over a matter of unpaid wages had fallen out with this mighty purveyor of amusement.

It pleased Muldoon to twit his old employer about the past. He had seen the yellow come out in Nafferton once. He was of the type who never forget such things. Deliberately he asked his next question.

"Yuh ain't seen Big Pierre lately, have yuh?" insinuation dripping from his mouth.

He saw that he struck home. Nafferton had not been the only one who heard the question. He waited until he was sure of his audience. From the safety of his own bar he dared anything.

"No, I haven't seen him," he muttered. "And by God, he better never set foot in this place. I'll have him thrown out quicker than the dirtiest bum that ever crawled."

"You'll find him quite an order," Muldoon asserted. "But I guess he ain't spending much time up river any more."

"Hell, no!" Nafferton shot back. "Down in Quebec, that's him. The Englishman has gone home, so he gets his chance now."

Lazy breathed asthmatically as he stood with his back propped up to the bar. He regarded Nafferton with pity.

"Meaning just what?" he whispered.

"Meaning Vallois' kid," Nafferton snapped back. "That's what I mean!"

Lazy regarded him as though he were beyond hope. He searched Nafferton's eyes to find some faint hint of a brain behind them, but gave up in disgust. He turned to the bar and finished his drink before he spoke.

The little audience who had overheard the conversation eyed Lazy expectantly. His personality dominated them as though they were peasants. He wiped his moustache with his hand. In the very same tone one uses to a child he addressed Nafferton. He shook his head as he spoke.

"You're a naughty, stupid boy, Naffy. You make even me blush."

Nafferton mocked him sarcastically as he started to leave. Lazy hung back for a second.

"My cute friend," he whispered, "I'd just as soon agree to let that Swede bar-keep of yours shoot dimes out of my mouth as to have uttered those words of yours. I've got an awful idea they'll lead you to the undertaker."

Lazy waddled out. Nafferton showed his teeth in a nasty grin, and the crowd, sensing the incident was over, turned to more exciting diversion.

Like the dog that chased the cat, that ate the rat, and so forth, Muldoon told MacNab and MacNab told another. And it followed that the day came when someone told Pierre.

The big Frenchman had wintered at the Post. He had stayed on in Quebec long after the week Duncan had thought it would take to arrange for the material for the mine. Pierre had been secretly well pleased at that turn of affairs.

He had found Marcette a goddess. In his clumsy way he had tried to deceive her about the hardships and depths to which Jim had sunk before he had found him. It had taken all of his patience to make her accept her share of the mine. That once accomplished, he set forth on a riotous tour of extravagance. Marcette accused him of trying to buy all the pretty things in Quebec for her.

She had sung for him and it seemed to Pierre that a hundred songbirds could not have made more melody. All too soon, Duncan had completed his arrangements and taken him away. Pierre had given her his promise that he would be down to take her back in the spring.

His going had left Marcette blue and lonesome. She knew the sacrifice Pierre Vallois made in letting her stay away from him for the long winter. That she had wealth now, and the promise of a future for her voice, did not suffice to make her happy. She had wanted riches and culture and knowledge for Jim's sake. But she was too young and full of life to be forever downcast. Inevitably, new interests engrossed her attention. Before she realized it, March was at hand.

The winter had not passed so quickly for Pierre. By Christmas he had completed all of the things Duncan had outlined. He was miserable for lack of something to do. With a joyous thrill he had awakened to the booming of the ice jam on the river. A week more and it would be free.

And as he waited there, impatient to be off, Mattagami, the Cree, came in from Trois Riviers with the mail and the whisper of Nafferton's boast.

Immediately life grew rosy for Pierre. Here was something to do. From the bottom of his heart he was thankful that the man had turned up. Once for all the score between them would be settled this time. From the Cree, he learned all he could of Nafferton. No waiting now for MacNab.

In silence he patched and gummed his canoe. He donned his old woods-clothes again. He took no one into his confidence. Overnight he invented an excuse for his going.

Once on the river he sent the canoe along at lightning speed, testing his muscles to the breaking point. It made him smile. The old strength was still there!

Long before he reached Trois Riviers he knew that only one of them would come out of this affair alive. It was best so.

When he beached his canoe it was supper-time. In the grey shadows he thought to slip away from the river unobserved and wait until the night crowd filled Nafferton's place.

222

But a pair of eyes had seen Pierre. They belonged to Lazy. He only marveled that the man had come so soon. He went to Nafferton's earlier than usual this night, his little ferret eyes roaming about alert and expectant.

When would the play begin?

CHAPTER
TWENTY-EIGHT

La Longue Traverse

Ten, half-past ten — time went on and nothing happened. The place was crowded. Nafferton stood in back of the bar, near the entrance, playing solitaire. Ten feet away old Lazy lounged, back against the railing as usual, his elbows caught on the edge of the bar. He had looked away for only an instant, yet when his eyes returned to Nafferton, the Frenchman was there, only the bar between them. Like a ghost he had glided in — no noise, no theatricals. Seconds dragged by. Lazy wondered if Nafferton would ever look up.

Almost to the last card the Englishman played out his game. The big Frenchman, watching the small white hands gliding over the pasteboards, saw them tremble. His own mouth tightened.

Whether or not it was the hypnosis of Lazy's stare, or a psychic influence warning him of danger, something told Nafferton Pierre was there. Long before he looked up he was sure of it. He knew he was watched. Both his hands were on the bar. He wondered if he could get his gun in time.

In the corner his band was ripping out a syncopated tune. The girls and their heavy-booted companions either sang or danced or kept time to its beat. He tried to give his bartenders the office — that signal with the lips peculiar to the underworld.

Again and again he tried it as though he pondered which card to lay next. He was embarrassed by his own riches. No one heard. Perspiration began to ooze from his forehead. Lazy could see where it dampened his hair. The man's face was deathly white. In a very frenzy of fear he looked up. The eyes of Pierre Baptiste ground back into his own.

Once he licked his dry lips, and then his hand went for the gun on his hip. Quicker than he, Pierre dashed the remains of Nafferton's whiskey and soda into his face. Nafferton's gun barked. Pierre felt the bullet tear its way through the muscle of his left forearm.

Two giant hands reached over the top of the bar. Then Nafferton was caught in a vise. A tug, a steeling of those mighty arms and he was bodily dragged and lifted from his shelter until he stood before the big Pierre. In his flight across the bar he had dropped his revolver.

Beseechingly he turned to see where his cohorts were. They were coming on the run. The sound of the exploding pistol had thrown the place into a panic.

Pierre saw them coming, too, in their hands whatever weapon they could lay on to — a gun, a bung-starter, a chair. And as he braced himself for the attack he saw a miracle happen.

Between Nafferton and himself and the on-rushing crowd there stood Lazy. Pierre saw his arm twitch with incredible swiftness. When it came forth from his vest

225

the great hulk held a derringer in his pudgy hand. The faro dealer ran right into it. It gored his stomach as Lazy cried to him to drop his gun. He obliged instantly. Lazy kicked it in back of himself. The interruption had stopped the crowd's mad gallop. He waved them back.

"This little toy might go off and hurt somebody," he purred, "if you get me all excited." He reached for his hip. "But this one here would blow a hole right clean through a man."

In his other hand he held a heavy forty-five.

"Now, none of you folks are going to get rough, cause life don't mean a damn thing to me, and most of you have got your mind pretty well sot on it."

As he talked Pierre and Nafferton faced each other. It was unbelievable to either of them that Lazy should have taken a hand in this.

Nafferton edged to the gun Lazy had kicked to the floor. Pierre's back was to the street. He faced the crowd. The blood flowed from his injured arm. It ran down his clothes. He could hear it dripping on the floor. But he dared not attend to it. He had blood to lose. He gritted his teeth as the pain began shooting through his body.

A movement in the crowd attracted him. An evil face crept along behind the polished bar. There was a gun in the man's hand. It was McGurk, Nafferton's major-domo.

Lazy saw him then, too. A man could not miss at that distance. McGurk's gun roared. A second later Lazy's forty-five spat its flame into the man's face. McGurk pitched headlong to the floor; flat on his face he lay; dead before he had time to relax his grip on his gun.

Lazy coughed and a red stain grew on his soiled shirt front. McGurk had torn a hole through his lungs. The crowd held back now. To a soul they were white-faced. Lazy spoke to Pierre:

"Now go on, big fellow, and give him what's coming to him. I'll see that nobody interferes."

Across the room the now happy Mr. Muldoon stepped forth.

"I'll second the motion," he cried. He crossed over to where Lazy stood and faced the crowd. "Mac got you bad, didn't he?" he whispered. "What did yuh ever want to mix in this for?"

Lazy smiled until he resembled his old, Buddha-like self.

"Oh, I just had a whim to do one decent thing before I died — that's all."

The time had come when Nafferton had to fight. There was no running away now. He wondered if he could by any chance hold his enemy off. He was a big man himself. But fighting had always disgusted Nafferton. It never seemed to prove anything. In clubs and school he had boxed his share. If science mattered, he had a chance. Even now, when his life hung in the balance, he tried in this fashion to belittle big Pierre.

He had two good arms though. That was a definite fact. Warily he circled until he fought at the injured arm. Pierre swung a thrashing blow for his jaw. Nafferton ducked under it, and sank his right into the big man's stomach. It made Pierre wince.

Skilfully Pierre led him to try it again. This time the injured arm shot out and up. It caught Nafferton a glancing blow on the side of the head. For a second it lifted him clear of the floor. Where Pierre's fist had landed a smear of blood remained. Unconsciously the Englishman felt his torn ear before he struck back.

With both of his hands in front of him, he rushed at Pierre like a mad man. The Frenchman had time to plant himself. Straight to the jaw his mighty right arm shot. Nafferton's head snapped back. There was a crack of splintering bone as he sank like a log. Blood flowed from his nose and mouth. Muldoon doused him with a bucket of water. Groggily he tried to sit up.

Pierre reached down with one hand and dragged him to his feet. Holding him there with his outstretched injured arm, he beat Nafferton's face until it was past recognition. When he had tired of that he lifted the wretch above his head and threw him through the very swinging doors Nafferton had vowed would some day see him treated in this fashion.

Through the opening at the bottom of the doors they could see the battered wreck lying in the gutter to which he had rolled.

Pierre was a sight. Torn, and covered with his own and Nafferton's blood, he was a gory picture. The fight had not tapped his strength, but the loss of blood from his arm was beginning to send a pallor to his face.

Swaying slightly from side to side he turned to Lazy. Lazy's own face was white; but from the chest down he was dyed a crimson red.

228

"Well done," he grinned at Pierre. "I'm good for ten minutes yet. Hike now."

For half a minute Pierre continued to stare at the man who had saved his life that night. Without Lazy's aid he would have long since joined McGurk. He smiled at him. Lazy smiled back. They both understood. There was no need for talk.

Pierre turned and the swinging doors hid him from view for a second. Then they saw him bend and throw the inert Nafferton over his shoulder as though he were a sack of flour.

Long before Lazy sank lifeless to the floor Pierre drove his canoe down the river. Huddled before him lay Nafferton.

By morning he had come to where the sloughs and swamps drain into the river. All day long he threaded his way among them. Night came, and he stopped where he was until the moon arose. Then he went on. Never once did he speak to the groaning beast before him. Neither water nor food had they tasted all that twenty-four hours.

Morning found them in an untracked waste. No hill or mountain marked the distant horizon. Water showed in little pools wherever one looked, the green, caribou moss cleverly hiding the muskegs. Walking was next to impossible.

Pierre got Nafferton to his feet. The dried, blackened blood, with which they were both covered, made them look ghastly. Piece by piece he stripped the clothing from the man until he stood arrayed in only his trousers. Speech came to Nafferton as he began to realize what faced him — *La Longue Traverse*.

He had heard of men led off like this and left to wander to their death — starvation, insanity, the tortures of a million flies on their naked bodies — it was hell in its worst form.

He fell to his knees and begged and cried for mercy. For answer, big Pierre pointed to the East.

"*La Longue Traverse!*" he roared.

"But I'll starve," shrieked Nafferton.

"You should have t'ought of dat a long tam' ago!"

"But the flies. In a week they'll be here to drive me mad. Let me keep my shirt. My God man have a little mercy!"

"You should t'ink 'bout dose flies when you lie 'bout me — when you lie 'bout Jim. *Allons!* — Go!" he cried. "*Allons!* — *Allons!*"

For ten minutes he sat and watched the battered figure as it drew away. Time and again, the wretch fell as he missed his footing among the muskegs. This was the end. There was no return possible this time.

Pierre swung his canoe about and headed for the river. Nafferton was left to pay the price.

CHAPTER
TWENTY-NINE

Out of the Silent North

It took seven months and eleven days to convince Jim Stannard that he must return to Canada. On the morning of the eleventh day he arose from the breakfast table determined to go at once. There was no happiness for him in England. Noon-time found him and his luggage aboard the boat train for Liverpool.

Once he had made the plunge, life came back with a thrill. He knew now a love of country such as England had never inspired within him. All he had done, that was worth while, had been accomplished in Canada. From the very depths he had ascended to his present estate. The very crudities, that democratic rubbing of shoulders which had once been so abhorrent, now appealed to him. He knew Canada for a land where men did things. How little the folks back home appreciated the mighty empire they were welding together for England's future use.

But beyond that love of the land which he had adopted for his own, there arose the vision of Marcette. He could go to her now. His hands were untied. Sometime, some way, he would make her forget and forgive him for the past. The optimism of youth was his.

The fog in the gulf had held them up at Gaspé Basin for hours. They should have docked at Quebec early that morning. Instead it was well on toward nine in the evening before he and his cross and impatient companions saw the lights of the terraced city rising before them.

The Château was almost deserted at this time of the evening. He had not cabled Duncan of his arrival. He found, however, that the engineer was registered there. He called his apartment but got no answer.

The after-theatre crowd was pouring into the beautiful dining room before he had finished his late dinner. As he sat there, idling over his cigarette and enjoying the crowd, a magnificent creature entered. People turned their heads. That smart, well-dressed throng made way for her as if she were a personage.

Her beautiful arms and glorious shoulders were creamy white against the filmy black of her gown. She would have conquered New York or Paris to-night. Pearly white teeth gleamed when she smiled; her large, dark eyes were pools of liquid fire.

A table had been reserved for her party. Fear seized Stannard as she advanced. He recognized Duncan and his wife. He saw Duncan pull out a chair for this radiant being. As she sat down, and the shaded table lights struck her face, Jim knew his eyes had not deceived him.

It was Marcette!

She had given her first concert that evening, her beauty and talent dimming the luster of her millions. She had not seen Stannard. But even as Jim sat there, pondering the change between this night and the evening at Old Peter's, Duncan saw him. Both arose automatically and Marcette recognized with a thrill the handsome chap advancing to her table.

She nodded to him as though they were the best of friends. For all the world, Stannard might have lunched with her that very day. She had acquired culture. No longer did she wear her heart exposed. But the sight and nearness of this man whom she had believed so far away, tested her mettle.

Work, that solace of hurt hearts, had laid its urge upon her. By unceasing effort she had sought forgetfulness. She had almost believed herself successful. Yet, as she gazed on Jim, there came to her one of those clairvoyant moments of life which told her that without him there was no happiness for her.

Duncan was delighted to see Stannard. He hastened to tell him of Marcette's success that evening.

"Where's Pierre Baptiste?" was Jim's immediate question. He looked at Marcette for his answer.

"I've expected him all day. He was to be here to take me home in the morning. If I did not know how efficient he was I'd really be worried."

"Oh, he will be here," Duncan asserted. "At the last minute he will come driving in. See if I am not right."

The orchestra began a throbbing, hauntingly familiar, waltz. In a daze, Marcette felt herself rising and being led away by the knight-errant of her dreams. His arms were about her. To the measured throb of the enchanting melody, they drifted off. Neither spoke. A word would have spoiled it.

People recognized them. Tongues wagged, scenting a romance. Before either knew it the night was gone. Mrs. Duncan took Marcette to her apartment.

Duncan asked Jim what his plans were.

"Well, we must go over that matter of the mill. I thought we would thresh things out and that I would go North with you."

"That's fine. We'll all be going to the station together in the morning, I suppose?" He queried.

"Delighted," Jim nodded.

"Then we will get down to business as soon as we return to the hotel."

The night was warm and Jim opened his windows and sat there building air castles. The unsophisticated girl he had left behind had come, like the butterfly from the chrysalis, a perfectly poised woman of the world. It was almost unbelievable.

He sat lost in amazement until Pierre's booming voice came ringing down the hallway. He rushed to the door to meet him. Here was the unchanged and unchanging being.

The greeting was effusive. The hearty hand-clasp and the quick survey of personality potent with feeling.

"Bagosh, you change, Jim!" Pierre laughed.

The sartorial graces of the big Frenchman were almost a disguise. But Jim only smiled.

"You've not changed any, Pierre."

"*Non, non.* I don' change. But the money, *mon jee,* I change heem. I jus' see Marcette. What's all dat I hear 'bout you not come wid us?"

234

"We've got to give a little time to business." Jim laughed.

"Huh!" Pierre snorted. "I go wake up Duncan. We do dat business right now. You wait!"

Forthwith he brought their manager, and partner, with his specifications for crushers, concentrators and so forth. By three o'clock, they knew they could not finish in time to allow Jim to catch the morning train. Even so, Pierre would not give up.

"M'sieu' Duncan, you come wid us as far as Chambord. Dat geeve us all day to talk t'ings over. I don' want to leave Jim behin'."

Duncan agreed to this plan before he left, and with the promise of all to meet at the station Pierre started to follow. Jim caught him by the arm. The big fellow ground his teeth in pain. Jim saw his misery.

"What's wrong with that arm, Pierre?"

He tried to pull it away.

"Oh, jus' little — accident dat's all."

Jim was not so easily satisfied. He pulled the coat sleeve up to the elbow.

"You've been shot," he cried.

"Maybe." Pierre grinned. "But don't tell Marcette — I tole her de train broke down. Dat's what make me late."

"Who did it?" Jim wanted to know. Pierre regarded him well before he answered.

"Nafferton!"

"Nafferton?" Jim echoed.

"*Oui* — he came back. But he's gone now."

And he proceeded to tell him what had happened.

235

"I tole you once, I keel dat man some day. You go to bed now, an' be at the depot on tam'."

Jim was waiting downstairs when Duncan and Marcette came in for breakfast. He had not closed his eyes. Nafferton's end brought strange memories. Breakfast was over without Pierre showing up. Marcette agreed with Duncan that he had undoubtedly gone off on some wild errand, so they drove to the station without him.

Jim paced the platform nervously as the minutes flew by. Duncan joined him. Together they scanned the streets that led to the station. Marcette's anxious eyes followed them. She saw them return. The conductor waved his hand and the little train began moving. At the last moment they saw the giant Frenchman running down hill. He stood in the street and waved his hand at them as he mopped his brow with his handkerchief. The rumble of his distant laugh reached them.

Pierre watched the train out of sight. The dismay his being left behind caused his friends was as nothing to the sinking of his own heart.

He had missed the train deliberately.

For all of his crude ways, he had sensed that a chance like this might never come again to bring Jim and Marcette together. That they could make the long trip to the Post without tearing down the barriers pride and duty had erected between them was impossible. Pierre knew that Jim was free now to choose whom he would. By themselves they would see a great deal of each other. He would be only in the way.

236

He sat in his room, alone for hours. He knew he had given the girl whom he loved better than life itself, to his friend. But it is written that some must fare alone.

After they had reconciled themselves to Pierre's absence, Jim and Duncan talked over many intricate details the erecting of their mill demanded. They tried to interest Marcette in the mysteries of cyaniding ore. But the beautiful country-side held her attention. From her window she saw herds of black and white Holsteins grazing contentedly in their sea-green meadows. At the little towns along the way every one was so dressed up in starchy white and Sunday black that the trip took on a holiday air. Everywhere she looked she found beauties to marvel at. Quebec province was at its best. Spring is no fairer even in Devon.

Evening came before they arrived at their destination. Duncan saw them on board. He would have to wait there overnight. Jim had received a telegram at Chambord from Pierre. It made him smile. It told him as plainly as words can, that his big friend had not missed the train by accident. He put it away as a treasure for future reference.

It was a sleepy company who journeyed North that night. Most of them had ridden for hours on the train. As the boat headed for Trois Riviers strange dreams came to two of its passengers.

Morning found a radiant Marcette. Through breakfast she was the same smiling, reserved person that Jim had seen that night at the Frontenac. In the long hours of afternoon they sat on deck and talked.

They had so much to talk about, these two, and yet they strangely avoided the thing both of them had ever before them.

It was Marcette who first touched the subject, although she was not conscious of it.

"Your making me an equal partner in the mine was a generous thing to do," she said. "For a long time I did not see how I could accept."

"It was the least I could do," Jim answered moodily. "We have misunderstood each other so often — I'm glad you didn't misunderstand me in this. It seemed small pay for all you had done. I've tried a thousand times to find words that would let me tell you how I have regretted my mistakes. I went home to get away from them. England drove me mad."

He paused to contemplate the scene before him.

"Lord, how I hated this land, once! It's home to me now, though. I want to help in its progress. I want to be a part of it. It seems to me to be the only way that I can earn your forgiveness."

"You will earn more than forgiveness," Marcette answered. She placed her hand on his where it rested on the railing. "It is such a small thing — not to forgive. One cannot be small and love this land." Marcette looked away for a spell before she finished. "I forgave you long ago. Remains now only forgetfulness. And when I see you so keen and alive, so anxious to help in the development of this great land — well, I somehow feel, that forgetfulness cannot be long delayed."

Marcette went to her cabin just before dinner, leaving Jim to smoke his pipe in silence. More simply than he could have managed it, she had opened the way to a new understanding between them.

He repeated her words, "one cannot be small and love this land." What a great truth they held. For the first time in years he was really happy. The westering sun smiled back at him as if it, too, rejoiced.

The moon came up as the boat ploughed along. The evening was warm. A million crickets and katydids called from the forests that lined the banks of the river. The air was sweet and resinous with the pungent smell of fir and cedar. On the lower deck, piled high with freight, men sat and smoked. From the railing where they stood, Jim and Marcette could see the glow of their pipes.

Just how it was accomplished, neither one of them ever knew. They had been standing there for half an hour. Without saying a word — just drinking in the beautiful night, when Jim sensed that she leaned close to him. Unconsciously his arm poised as it made to steal about her. She was so close. The vagrant wind blew a strand of her hair across his face. The impulse to draw her into his arms and never let her go was maddening.

Their eyes sought each other's. Marcette's lips trembled.

"M'sieu' Jim," she murmured so low he barely heard. Thus she had called him in the days of long ago at Roubideaux. Whole aeons of time were removed in that meeting of the eyes. Sorrow, and pain — all memories of the past were gone. Closer and closer, he

239

pressed her to him, his hands crushing hers within his own.

They stood for minutes before his head bent and their lips met in their first kiss. It rested upon them like a benediction.

Down below a boy sang. The words of his song drifted up to them:

> "My roaming days are over,
> I've got to settle down,
> With a little girl in a
> One-horse, country town."

They smiled. The song was suddenly stilled. Everything was at peace.

From the boiler-room came the glow of the fires as the stokers shoveled the coal. It lighted up the forests through which they passed. On the bank they saw a white-tailed buck bound away as the red glow reached the spot where he drank.

Jim drew forth the telegram he had received from Pierre, smoothed it out and held it so Marcette could read.

Her eyes grew misty. She knew now why the mighty Pierre Baptiste had missed the train, for the message read:

"Congratulations and best, best wishes."

And she breathed a silent prayer for the great man who so gladly broke his own heart, that she might be happy.